Sandra L. Caron, Ph.D.
The University of Maine

P9-ELQ-579

SEX AROUND

THE WORLD

Cross-Cultural Perspectives
on Human Sexuality

Third Edition

Custom Publishing

New York   Boston   San Francisco

London   Toronto   Sydney   Tokyo   Singapore   Madrid

Mexico City   Munich   Paris   Cape Town   Hong Kong   Montreal

Printed in the United States of America

10 9 8 7 6 5 4 3 2 1

2008280005

KA

**Pearson
Custom Publishing**
is a division of

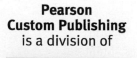

www.pearsonhighered.com

ISBN 10: 0-536-42444-6
ISBN 13: 978-0-536-42444-0

CONTENTS

PREFACE

Most people could not say that a day goes by in which they do not encounter some aspect of sexuality. We are confronted with issues pertaining to birth control, abortion, AIDS, gay/lesbian rights, and so on in our homes, schools, places of employment and even within our own thoughts. Human sexuality is a widely-discussed topic that often becomes the center of conversation in one form or another. Yet, this topic of discussion should not be limited to one's familiar habitat.

Technological advances in communication and the manner in which we access information has linked us to cultures across the world in ways our ancestors never fathomed. The booming popularity of the Internet, for example, allows us the opportunity to connect with people and places of foreign domain via our own personal computers. College students are quite familiar with this convenient method of communicating since most institutions provide access to the Internet through computer clusters often located in campus libraries. These advances have undoubtedly transformed our world into a global village. Therefore, it has become necessary to learn more about other cultures' social, political, economic, and religious values—and yes, sexual attitudes as well.

The purpose of this book is to serve as a quick reference to facts about cross-cultural perspectives in human sexuality. It can also serve as a supplement to courses taught in human sexuality and cross-cultural psychology or development. It is important to educate Americans of the diverse attitudes and behaviors that exist across the world because knowledge about another culture's views assists us in gaining perspective on our own sexuality.

In addition, this book will help to lessen the ethnocentrism used by many Americans when judging other cultures. In other words, it will assist people in understanding that what goes on in America is not the norm and that our own values should not be treated as the standard by which to judge others. It is natural for Americans to think in such a manner since our country is geographically isolated from nearly 200 nations that exist around the world. Yet, we should not forget that we are indeed a Multicultural nation and a melting pot of different beliefs and practices as well as sexual attitudes. For college students, this fact is apparent since 1 out of every 10 students in American colleges comes from other countries. After reading this book, students will learn that sexual behaviors differ among various cultural groups and that there is no set standard for what is considered normal.

This book covers the basic aspects of sexuality for 44 different countries. A brief overview of each country is provided, including information on population, ethnicity, religions, per capita income (this is the GNP divided by the total population, not average income), etc. It is important to have some background knowledge since the environment we live in often plays a major role in shaping our attitudes on sexuality. Pertinent data is then presented on the following issues: sexual activity, contraception, abortion, sex education, sexually transmitted infections, sexual orientation, prostitution, and pornography. In addition, data for teenage pregnancies, births, and abortions have been complied and presented for some of the developed countries at the beginning of the book. A scan of this data reveals that teenage pregnancy is more common in the United States than in most other industrialized countries. Since each chapter follows the same content outline, the reader can easily draw comparisons between each country.

For instance, among industrialized nations, the United States has one of the leading pregnancy rates for teenagers ages 15–19. For every 1,000 American teenage girls, 84 become pregnant each year. Experts who have become long-time advocates of sex education argue that teaching teenagers about human sexuality could help to diminish the pregnancy rate. However, in America, only 23 states require formal teaching about human sexuality. And in many states, these mandates or polices preclude teaching about such subjects as intercourse, abortion, masturbation, homosexuality, condoms, and safer sex.

In comparison, the Netherlands' teenage pregnancy rate stands at 12 per 1,000 teenagers. Ironically, lessons in human sexuality are available at all levels of school education and offered through youth clubs.

Another striking difference relates to abortions. As American politicians continue the controversial debate on the issue, Russians view abortion as a primary method of birth control. On average, every woman born in the Russia Federation has two or three abortions. It was also the first country in the world to legalize abortion. In Ireland, abortion is illegal except in cases where the mother's life is in danger. In February 1992, a 14-year-old rape victim was prevented by the High Court to travel to Britain for an abortion procedure. This eventually led to a Supreme Court ruling that grants women the freedom to travel abroad and obtain abortions. Presently, an estimated 6,000 Irish women journey to Britain for abortions each year.

While detecting the remarkable differences in sexual behaviors among these 44 countries, the reader will also discover some fascinating similarities. For example, most countries have established a minimum age of sexual consent. Adult pornography is regulated by the government and certain laws control access to sexual material. And in all countries, incest is considered a taboo.

Among the following pages, you are presented with an opportunity to explore various perspectives in human sexuality. The facts presented in this book speak for themselves: We live in a world composed of cultural diversity. It is when we perceive the views of others, we also develop a better understanding of the values and behaviors that exist within our own culture and learn to accept our role in the global village.

About the Author

Dr. Sandra L. Caron is Professor of Family Relations/Human Sexuality at the University of Maine. She teaches both undergraduate and graduate courses in family studies and human sexuality. She is also a member of the Women's Studies faculty. In the summers she teaches a course entitled, *Human Sexuality in Europe*, which provides students with an international perspective on sexual and reproductive health issues. In this course U.S. college students travel to London, Amsterdam and Stockholm to meet with sexuality professionals and see firsthand how other countries deal with teen pregnancy, abortion, birth control, sexuality education, as well as public policy issues related to HIV/AIDS, sexual orientation and prostitution.

Dr. Caron is the founder and director of three nationally recognized peer education programs: "Athletes for Sexual Responsibility," "The Greek Peer Educator Program," and "Male Athletes Against Violence." She writes a regular column on sexuality for the campus newspaper entitled, *Sex Matters*, has been the host of a radio show by that same name on the campus radio station, and hosts a national website for college students entitled collegesextalk.com (*http://www.collegesextalk.com*).

In 2002 Dr. Caron received the Presidential Public Service Achievement Award for the University of Maine. In 1999 she received the Margaret Vaughn Award from the Family Planning Association of Maine for her outstanding contribution to sexuality education. She is the 1998 recipient of the Presidential Outstanding Teaching Award for the University of Maine. In 1997, she became Maine's first recipient of the Faculty-Student Centered Award.

She has been an active member of the American Association of Sex Educators, Counselors, and Therapists, and the Society for the Scientific Study of Sexuality for over 20 years.

Her research and publications have focused on the social-sexual development of young people, with an emphasis on sexual decision-making, contraceptive use, safer sex, sexual assault, sexuality education, and cross cultural perspectives. In addition to her many scholarly publications in research journals, she has authored two books, *Cross-Cultural Perspectives on Human Sexuality* and *Sex Matters for College Students: FAQs in Human Sexuality, 2nd edition* (published in 2007 by Prentice Hall).

TEENAGE BIRTH, ABORTION, PREGNANCY DATA

Rates of adolescent birth, abortion and pregnancy per year (per 1,000 women aged 15–19) and abortion ratio (per 100 pregnancies), by developed country

Country	Birth Rate	Abortion Rate	Pregnancy Rate	Abortion Ratio
Australia	19.8	23.8	43.7	54.1
Austria	15.6	u	u	u
Belgium	9.1	5.0	14.1	35.6
Bulgaria	49.6	33.7	83.3	40.4
Canada	24.2	21.2	45.4	47.1
Czech Republic	20.1	12.3	32.4	38.1
Denmark	8.3	14.4	22.7	62.6
England and Wales	28.4	18.6	46.9	40.2
Finland	9.8	10.7	20.5	52.9
France	10.0	10.2	20.2	51.2
Germany	12.5	3.6	16.1	23.0
Greece	13.0	u	u	u
Hungary	29.5	29.6	59.1	50.3
Ireland	15.0	4.2	19.2	21.9
Israel	18.0	9.8	27.9	35.3
Italy	6.9	5.1	12.0	42.9
Japan	3.9	6.3	10.1	61.9
Netherlands	8.2	4.0	12.2	33.8
New Zealand	34.0	20.0	54.0	37.2
Northern Ireland	23.7	4.8	28.4	17.0
Norway	13.5	18.7	32.3	59.2
Poland	21.1	u	u	u
Portugal	20.9	u	u	u
Romania	42.0	32.0	74.0	42.9
Russian Federation	45.6	56.1	101.7	56.1
Scotland	27.1	14.5	41.6	37.2
Slovak Republic	32.3	11.1	43.3	25.5
Spain	7.8	4.5	12.3	36.7
Sweden	7.7	17.2	24.9	69.6
Switzerland	5.7	u	u	u
United States	54.4	29.2	83.6	34.9

Source: Singh S and Darroch JE, Adolescent pregnancy and childbearing: Levels and trends in developed countries, *Family Planning Perspectives*, 2000, 32(1): 14–23.

AUSTRALIA

AUSTRALIA
POPULATION: 20,264,082

CAPITAL: **CANBERRA**
POPULATION: 327,700

Major Cities:	Sydney, Melbourne, Brisbane, Perth, Adelaide
Ethnic Groups:	Caucasian 92%; Asian 7%; Aboriginal 1%
Languages:	English (official) and aboriginal language
Major Religions:	Roman Catholic 26%, Anglican 21%, other Christian 21%
GDP per capita (PPP):	$31,900
Urban Population:	85%
Infant Mortality:	5 per 1,000 births
Life Expectancy:	Females: 84 years; Males: 78 years
Adult Literacy:	100%
Health Care System:	1 physician per 434 people. Universal health insurance has been available since 1984; private health insurance is also available.

References

❑ *The World Almanac and Book of Facts* (2006). NY: World Almanac Education Group.
❑ *The World Factbook http://www.cia.gov/cia/publications/factbook/* Accessed June 25, 2006.
❑ *World Reference Atlas* (2005). NY: Dorling Kindersley Publishing.

Sexual Activity[1]

❖ The age of consent in most states is 16 years old, with one exception: The age of consent for male-male sexual relations is 18 in Queensland.

Contraception[2]

❖ The most commonly used methods of contraception are the Pill, IUD, condom, and diaphragm.

❖ A major problem in Australia is premature discontinuation of contraceptives, usually due to side effects and dissatisfaction.

❖ Lack of education and religion also influence the utilization of contraceptives in Australia.

Abortion[3]

❖ Only South Australian and Northern Territory laws define lawful abortions. Other states and territories derive laws from judicial interpretation.

❖ All states permit abortions to save the life of the pregnant woman.

❖ All states and territories require that abortions be performed in a hospital and by licensed physicians.

❖ The Australian government health insurance covers abortions.

❖ All states except for Tasmania (Criminal Code Act of 1924) and Western Australia (Criminal Code Act of 1913) permit abortions on mental and physical health grounds.

❖ The maximum prison term for persons performing illegal abortions range from 10–15 years.

Sex Education[4]

❖ In 1992, the Health Minister released a report recommending installing condom vending machines in schools as part of sex education. Many state education officials agreed to read the report and considered integrating condom use and sexuality into their AIDS education material.

❖ At that time, schools run by the Roman Catholic Church agreed to focus on improving AIDS education but not sex education or condom use.

Sexually Transmitted Infections (including HIV)

❖ Australia was among the first countries in the world to report AIDS cases.[5]

❖ An estimated 16,000 people were living with HIV/AIDS in Australia in 2005.[5]

❖ The proportion of women among reported cases has been gradually increasing, from 0% in 1983 to 10% in 2000.[5]

❖ HIV infection in children remains rare.[5]

❖ After declining in the late 1990s, annual new HIV diagnoses are approaching earlier levels again, and numbered some 820 in 2004. Newly acquired HIV infections (largely attributable to unprotected sex, mostly between men) are increasing, which plausibly reflects a revival of sexual risk behavior.[6]

❖ Overall rates for other STI (Sexually Transmitted Infections) have declined since the mid-1980s. However, rates of STI among indigenous populations continue to be substantially higher (by a factor of 10 to 100 times) than in the non-indigenous population.[5]

Sexual Orientation

❖ In 1970 homosexuals established an open organization to demand recognition, equal and just treatment before the law, and an end to discrimination.[7]

❖ In 1972 South Australia became the first state to partially decriminalize homosexual acts.[7]

❖ By 1987 all the states of Australia decriminalized homosexual acts except for Queensland.[7]

- In 1992 the Australian cabinet ended its ban on homosexuals in the military.[8]
- In March 2002, with the passage of the Acts Amendment (Lesbian and Gay) Law Reform Bill 2001, Western Australia, no longer lagged far behind other Australian states in its recognition of rights on the basis of sexual orientation, but rather set a progressive example. This bill contained measures that equalized the age of consent for all persons at 16 years; repealed the Gross Indecency Law, which targeted male-male sexual activity in public places; included sexual orientation as a protected category in the State's Equal Opportunity Act of 1984; provided access to adoption and in vitro fertilization treatment for same-sex couples; and granted additional rights to same-sex couples.[9]
- In June 2006 Australia's conservative national government has overruled a local law allowing gay marriages. The Australian Capital Territory (ACT) became the first part of the country to legally recognize gay relationships. But now the federal government has stepped in to invalidate the new law.[10]

Prostitution[11]

- It is not illegal to sell sex in Australia.
- In all jurisdictions, except New South Wales, street prostitution is illegal and workers may be arrested for soliciting or loitering for the purposes of prostitution.
- In New South Wales, Australia, any person over the age of 18 may offer to provide sexual services in return for money. In Victoria, Australia, a person who wishes to run a prostitution business must have a license. Prostitutes working for themselves in their own business, as prostitutes in the business, must be registered. Individual sex workers are not required to be registered or licensed.
- Except of New South Wales and Victoria, no state penalizes the clients of prostitutes.

Pornography[12]

- Child pornography in Australia is a federal offense and is punishable under Australian law.
- Australia classifies all films and literature to protect children from pornographic material.
- The classifications range from G (general exhibition) to X (explicit sex: restricted to adults 18 and over).
- The government cannot impose restrictions on what can be filmed, but can restrict transportation of obscene material.
- X-rated videos are not illegal in Australia but to sell them commercially is illegal.

Resources

▶ Australian Association of Sex Educators, Counselors, and Therapists (AASERT), P.O. Box 346, Lane Cove, New South Wales 2066 Australia. Tel: 61-2-427-1292.

▶ Family Planning Australia, Lua Building, Suite 3, First Floor, 39 Geils C, P.O. Box 9026, Deakin, ACT 26000 Australia. Tel: 61-6-282-5298.

AUSTRIA

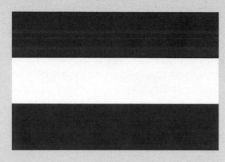

Major Cities:	Vienna, Graz, Linz, Salzburg, Innsbruck
Ethnic Groups:	Austrians 91%, former Yugoslavs 4% (includes Croatians, Slovenes, Serbs, and Bosniaks)
Languages:	German (official)
Major Religions:	Roman Catholic 74%; Protestant 5%, Islam 4%
GDP per capita (PPP):	$32,700
Urban Population:	65%
Infant Mortality:	5 per 1,000 births
Life Expectancy:	Females: 82 years; Males: 76 years
Adult Literacy:	98%
Health Care System:	National health care system, with nearly universal access. 1 doctor per 230 persons.

References

❑ *The World Almanac and Book of Facts* (2006). NY: World Almanac Education Group.

❑ *The World Factbook* *http://www.cia.gov/cia/publications/factbook/* Accessed June 25, 2006.

❑ *World Reference Atlas* (2005). NY: Dorling Kindersley Publishing.

Sexual Activity

* Age of consent for heterosexual and homosexual relations is 14.[1]
* One third of the women have had sexual intercourse before the age of 16 years.[2]
* Twenty-four percent of 15–44 year olds have had at least one unplanned pregnancy, and 10% have had more than one.[2]

Contraception

* Vasectomies as well as vasectomy-reversal procedures are performed less frequently in Austria than in other European countries.[2]
* In general the standard of contraception in Austria is rather low; on average only every second Austrian woman uses contraceptives. No data is available on the use of prophylactics by Austrian men.[3]
* First Love is an Austrian FPA counseling center dedicated to helping young people. First Love offers free and confidential psychological counseling and gynecological examinations to young women one afternoon per week.[4]
* Contraceptives are not supplied free of charge through the State services. Condoms are advertised and available in pharmacies and condom vending machines also exist. There are no practical obstacles to obtaining contraceptives except for adolescents who may not be welcomed by all physicians.[5]
* Emergency contraception is licensed for use by prescription.[6]

Abortion

* Since January 1974 abortion on request within the first trimester of pregnancy has been exempt from punishment for the first time in Austrian history.[7]
* Although abortion within the first trimester is legal, access to abortion is still not guaranteed throughout Austria.

In several parts of the country it is difficult or simply impossible to obtain one because many physicians refuse to perform abortions for moral and/or religious reasons.[7]
* All abortions must be performed by a licensed physician. Doctors in private practices perform the majority of abortions.[7]
* The health care system pays for abortions performed for medical reasons.[8]
* RU-486 (Mifepristone) was approved for marketing in 1999.[9]

Sex Education[5]

* Sex education is legally regulated as part of the school curriculum and it is theoretically implemented in elementary, secondary, and higher education levels.
* The situation is not reflected in practice, though some sex education is available in some schools according to the willingness of the teaching staff. The mass media regularly features sex education programming.

Sexually Transmitted Infections (including HIV)[10]

* An estimated 10,000 people were living with HIV/AIDS in Austria at the end of 2003. One third of all AIDS cases got infected by injecting drugs, about half are through male-to-male sex.
* Testing is mandatory in all blood/plasma organ donors, as well as for prostitutes.
* Data on HIV are available through those screening programs. There is no national register for HIV cases.
* Several surveys have been conducted among IDU (Intravenous Drug Users) and prisoners. HIV prevalence among IDU increased from 13% in 1986 to 27% in 1990 in Vienna. In Innsbruck, prevalence reached 44% in the time period of 1985–1990.

* Prevalence in prisons is estimated around 0.5% to 1.3%, 5 times higher than in the general population.
* Incidence of syphilis decreased in the late eighties to reach a stable level of 1–2.9 cases per 100,000; however there has been an increase to 5.2 cases per 100,000 in 2002.

Sexual Orientation

* Austria has a long history of criminalization and oppression of lesbians and gay men. In 1971, Austria was one of the last countries in Europe to repeal the total ban on homosexuality.[11]
* Until 1997, gay and lesbian organizations and publications were illegal under Sections 220 and 221 of the Penal Code.[11]
* Austria has a very poor record of anti-discrimination provisions in general and none at all to protect gays and lesbians from sexual-orientation-based discrimination. The Federal Constitution theoretically protects all citizens equally and requests that all citizens are treated equally before the law but daily experience and the jurisprudence of the courts show that this does not apply to sexual orientation discrimination.[11]
* Austria allows persons who engage in homosexual behavior to serve in the military.[12]

Prostitution

* Prostitution is legal in all but one province, Vorarlberl.[13]

* In Vienna, legalized prostitution is tightly controlled by the Board of the Viennese Public Health Service. Registered prostitutes are routinely screened for STI, such as syphilis, HIV, gonorrhea, Chlamydia, and yeast infections. Furthermore, cytological smears are obtained from the cervix and chest X-rays are performed at least once a year. Those found to be HIV-positive are prohibited from working.[14]

Pornography[15]

* Pornography is regulated through a federal law passed in 1990, "The Federal Act Against Obscene Publications and for the Protection of Youth Morally Endangered. In 1994, punishment for producing, selling, and possessing child pornography was written into law.
* The minimum age for a person buying soft porn/erotica, a *Playboy* magazine for instance, is 16 years. The minimum age for buying porn or entering an adult video store where hardcore pornography is available for rental or sale is 18 years. Violent content, including bestiality, sexual acts involving minors, and violent sexual acts is, of course, legally forbidden in Austria.
* Punishment is limited to those who produce or distribute obscene texts, pictures, or films or other obscene objects for profit. Possession or non-commercial exchanges of violent pornography is still permitted.

Resource

▶ Österreichische Gesellschaft für Familienplanung (ÖGF), Ignaz Semmelweis Frauenklinik, Bastiengasse 36–38, 1180 Vienna, Austria. Tel. +43 (1) 478 52 42. Website: *http://www.oegf.at/*

BELGIUM

BELGIUM

POPULATION: 10,379,067

CAPITAL: **BRUSSELS**

POPULATION: 1,750,600

Major Cities:	Antwerp, Ghent, Charleroi, Liege
Ethnic Groups:	Fleming 58%; Walloon 31%
Languages:	Dutch (official) 60%; French (official) 40%
Major Religions:	Roman Catholic 75%; Protestant, other 25%
GDP per capita (PPP):	$31,400
Urban Population:	97%
Infant Mortality:	5 per 1,000 births
Life Expectancy:	Females: 82 years; Males: 76 years
Adult Literacy:	99%
Health Care System:	Physicians: 1 per 270 persons.

References

❑ *The World Almanac and Book of Facts* (2006). NY: World Almanac Education Group.
❑ *The World Factbook* http://www.cia.gov/cia/publications/factbook/ Accessed June 25, 2006.
❑ *World Reference Atlas* (2005). NY: Dorling Kindersley Publishing.

Sexual Activity

❖ The age of consent is 16.[1]

❖ About one-third of young women begin having sex before age 18.[2]

Contraception

❖ Almost every woman obtaining an abortion is given a prescription for contraceptives following the procedure.[3]

❖ Contraceptive prevalence in Belgium is high. Results from a study of 1,050 women aged 15–44 showed that 68 percent use a contraceptive method.[3]

❖ Emergency contraception is available over-the-counter.[4]

Abortion

❖ Until April 1990 abortion was illegal in Belgium under all circumstances. However, a small group of health professionals had long provided high-quality abortion services in outpatient facilities and in hospitals.[3]

❖ The 1867 Belgian Penal Code, which defined the pre-1990 abortion law, was based on the Napoleonic Code of 1810, and it restricted abortion under all circumstances.[3]

❖ In April 1990 the Belgian Parliament approved a law that permits abortion within the first 12 weeks of pregnancy when a physician deems the woman to be in a "state of distress"—a condition that is legally undefined.[3]

❖ After 12 weeks of pregnancy, abortion can be performed if two physicians agree that the woman's health is in danger, or in cases of proved fetal malformation.[3]

❖ A six-day waiting period is required from the time of the request to the time of the procedure.[3]

❖ The Belgian legislation does not explicitly require parental consent for minors under the age of 18, but some abortion service providers try to obtain such consent, not differentiating abortion from other medical procedures that require consent.[3]

❖ In 1999, RU-486 (Mifepristone) was approved for marketing in Belgium.[5]

Sex Education

❖ In Belgium, health education and prevention comes under the responsibility of the Communities (French-speaking, Flemish and German-speaking), rather than that of the national state.[6]

❖ In Belgium, sex education is not particularly linked to a special school subject and it may be part of any subject.[7]

Sexually Transmitted Infections (including HIV)[8]

❖ Between the start of the epidemic and the end of June 2003, 16,371 people were diagnosed with HIV.

❖ There has been little variation in the number of cases diagnosed between 1986 and 1998; on average 2 to 3 cases were diagnosed per day.

❖ Among Belgian men, homosexual and bisexual relations are by far the most important transmission path, involving two out of three patients. Among women, heterosexual transmission clearly predominates.

❖ Approximately 6% of patients are intravenous drug users. IDU transmission is most prominent in young people; 17% of patients aged 15–24 are IDU.

❖ AIDS patients can be divided into two groups: those who have been living in Belgium for a long time and non-residents who were diagnosed shortly after arriving in the country. The profiles of the two groups are quite different. Among residents, mostly Belgian, the male/female ratio is much higher than among non-residents; more than two-thirds of the male residents had homosexual or bisexual contacts. Among the women, heterosexual contacts predominate; this is true also of non-resident patients, whatever their sex.

❖ Most patients live in the cities, especially Brussels, Antwerp and Liège.

Sexual Orientation

❖ The total ban on homosexuality was lifted in 1792.[9]

❖ In January 2003 Belgium passed a law similar to The Netherlands allowing same-sex marriage, but disallowing any adoptions.[9]

❖ There is no discrimination against gays in the military.[10]

Prostitution[11]

❖ Prostitution is illegal, but tolerated. Pimping and trade in women is prosecuted.

❖ Until the fifties, there was an official prostitution policy with registration and health checks. That was abolished, but certain cities have re-implemented this policy unofficially.

Pornography[1]

❖ The legal age for viewing pornography in Belgium is 18 years.

❖ Sex shops and peep shows are tolerated in larger cities.

Resources

▶ Fédération Laïque de Centres de Planning Familial (FLCPF), Rue de la Tulipe 34, 1150 Brussels, Belgium. Tel: 32 2 502 82 03. Website: *http://www.planningfamilial.net/*

▶ Sensoa, Meerssstraat 138B, 9000 Ghent, Belgium. Tel: 32 (9) 221 07 22. Website: *http://www.sensoa.be/*

BRAZIL

BRAZIL
POPULATION: 188,078,227

CAPITAL: BRASILIA
POPULATION 2,160,100

Major Cities:	Sao Paulo, Rio de Janeiro, Belo Horizonte
Ethnic Groups:	White (Include. Portuguese, German, Italian, Spanish, Polish) 54%; Mixed Black and White 38%; Black 6%
Languages:	Portuguese (official); Plus Spanish, English, French
Major Religions:	Roman Catholic 74%, Protestant 15%
GDP per capita (PPP):	$8,400
Urban Population:	81%
Infant Mortality:	37 per 1,000 live births
Life Expectancy:	Females: 68 years; Males: 59 years
Adult Literacy:	85%
Health Care:	Publicly funded clinics and health centers; 1 physician per 681 people.

References
❑ *The World Almanac and Book of Facts* (2006). NY: World Almanac Education Group.
❑ *The World Factbook* http://www.cia.gov/cia/publications/factbook/ Accessed June 25, 2006.
❑ *World Reference Atlas* (2005). NY: Dorling Kindersley Publishing.

Sexual Activity

❖ Age of consent is 14 years old.[1]

❖ Median age of first intercourse is 16 years old; approximately 25% of women have had sex before age 18.[2]

❖ 15% of the 14,000 11–14 year olds who become pregnant each year in Brazil have been raped.[3]

Contraception

❖ In 1979 the advertising of contraceptives was decriminalized and the distribution of contraceptives was permitted.[4]

❖ Currently, 76.6% of Brazilian women in a stable relationship use some form of contraception. Sterilization and the contraceptive pill are the most frequently used methods.[4]

❖ In 1992, 7.5 million women were sterilized during cesarean operations.[4]

Brazil passed the Family Planning Law in 1996, which prohibits forcing or requiring anyone to practice family planning as a means of population control.[5]

❖ Within the public sector contraceptives are delivered through the PAISM and PROSAD programs.[6]

❖ Emergency contraceptives are available in Brazil in the form of Norlevo/ Postinor-2.[6]

Abortion

❖ The performance of an abortion constitutes a criminal act in Brazil, but is permitted to save the life of the women and to terminate a pregnancy resulting from rape.[7]

❖ Although abortion is outlawed in Brazil except in rare circumstances, the country has one of the highest abortion rates in the developing world. The Health Ministry estimates that 31 per cent of all pregnancies end in abortion, the equivalent of 1.4 million abortions a year. Botched abortions are the fourth-leading cause of maternal deaths in Brazil.[8]

❖ In 2005, the government sent a bill to Congress to legalize abortion and proponents believe it will be come legal in the near future.[8]

❖ Misoprastol is used by some women to induce an abortion. This is an ulcer drug that until 1991 was sold without a prescription.[9]

Sex Education[10]

❖ In 1993 a poll implemented by the mainstream newspaper in Brazil showed that 86% of the respondents wanted sex education in schools.

❖ One organization known as GTPOS has implemented sexual guidance programs.

❖ GTPOS believes that sexual guidance programs should begin in preschool and continue through high school.

❖ GTPOS has trained teachers and focuses on education as well as prevention.

Sexually Transmitted Infections (including HIV)[11]

❖ Brazil has one of the highest rates of AIDS in the world.

❖ Brazil is home to more than one-third of the total number of people living with HIV in Latin America (620,000 adults and children) and national HIV prevalence was 0.5% in 2005.

❖ The HIV epidemic in Brazil has changed substantially in the past 10 years regarding involvement of IDUs. In the mid-1990s, IDUs contributed almost 30% of all AIDS cases. However, IDUs are represented in the HIV/AIDS epidemic in a very specific pattern across the country. In certain areas, IDUs contribute almost 50% of all AIDS cases, suggesting that the pattern of the HIV/AIDS epidemic in Brazil is heterogeneous and has changed according to time, geographic region, and subpopulations affected.

❖ In 2001, estimates of incidence and prevalence were developed for other

STI. Of the STI examined, HPV prevalence was highest.

Sexual Orientation[12]

❖ Homosexual behavior between consenting adults is not a criminal offense, except with regard to the Armed Forces.

❖ Brazil does display very ambiguous opinions regarding homosexuality: on one hand it is a nation with an exuberant gay culture. On the other hand, an attempt to include the prohibition of discrimination on the grounds of sexual orientation in the Federal Constitution was defeated by 429 to 130 votes in 1987. A second, unsuccessful, campaign to amend the constitution took place in 1993.

❖ In 1998, the President of the Brazilian Supreme Court, in a meeting with LGBT activists, came out in support of amending the Constitution to include protection from discrimination on the grounds of sexual orientation, registered partnerships "not constituting matrimony", the end of the ban on lesbians and gays in the military, and protection for people who are transgender.

Prostitution

❖ Prostitution is not illegal but it is illegal to operate a brothel, to rent premises to prostitutes, exploit children or live off the earnings of a prostitute.[13]

❖ Child prostitution is an expanding market in Brazil. There are between 250,000 and 500,000 children involved in the sex trade.[14]

❖ Some children work in brothels and service 10 to 15 clients a day, and some are sold to ranchers who gang rape them to death.[14]

Pornography[15]

❖ Legal age for viewing pornography in Brazil is 18 years old.

❖ The military regime that dominated Brazil from 1964 to 1985 repressed the publication of erotica and sexually explicit films. Since 1985, there has been a great surge in the number of pornography shops and erotic films, videos, and publications.

❖ Presently both hard- and soft-core pornography is easily accessible in Brazil. Both television and cinema theaters exhibit erotic films.

❖ Male actors in local movies must wear condoms in penetration scenes. All actors must be 18 or older.

❖ Scenes showing sex with children or animals are strictly avoided, as is any depiction of sadomasochism, although sexual cruelty and violence may sometimes be shown.

Resources

▶ BEMFAM Av. República do Chile #230, 17º andar, Centro - Rio de Janeiro, Rio de Janeiro, 20.031-170, Brazil. Tel: (55-21) 3861-2400. Website: *http://www.bemfam.org.br/*

▶ Brazilian Association of Sexology (AB-SEX), Associação Brasileira de Sexologia, Dr. Sergio Luiz G. de Freitas, M.D., President, Rua Tamandare, 693 - Conj. 77, 01525-001 Sao Paulo - SP - Brasil.

▶ Brazilian Sexual Education Association, Associação Brasileira de Educação Sexual, Alameda Itu, 859 - Apto 61, 01421-000 São Paulo - SP - Brasil.

▶ Brazilian Society of Human Sexuality, Sociedade Brasileira de Sexualidade Humana, Av. N.S. Copacabana, 1072 - s. 703, 22020-001. Rio de Janeiro - RJ - Brasil.

BULGARIA

BULGARIA

POPULATION: 7,385,367

CAPITAL: SOFIA
POPULATION: 1,088,700

Major Cities:	Sofia, Ploudiv, Vaina, Burgas
Ethnic Groups:	Bulgarian 84%, Turk 9%, Roman 5%
Languages:	Bulgarian (official)
Major Religions:	Bulgarian Orthodox 83%, Muslim 12%
GDP per capita (PPP):	$9,600
Urban Population:	69%
Infant Mortality:	15 per 1,000 births
Life Expectancy:	Females: 75 years; Males: 68 years
Adult Literacy:	98%
Health Care:	1 physician per 287 persons. During the 1990's Bulgaria began allowing free choice of a family doctor. They began accepting money and medicine from Western countries.

References
❑ *The World Almanac and Book of Facts* (2006). NY: World Almanac Education Group.
❑ *The World Factbook* *http://www.cia.gov/cia/publications/factbook/* Accessed June 25, 2006.
❑ *World Reference Atlas* (2005). NY: Dorling Kindersley Publishing.

Sexual Activity

❖ The percentage of teen girls under the age of 16 who give birth is higher than the U.S., Poland and Soviet Union, thus indicating the early engagement in sexual activity.[1]

❖ The age of consent for heterosexual sex is 14 years old; for homosexuals it is 18.[2]

Contraception

❖ There is little opposition from the Orthodox Church regarding the use of contraception and there are adequate supplies on the market, but the lack of use stems from the high price.[1]

❖ The cost of one cycle of pills is the same as the cost of an abortion.[3]

❖ There are an abundance of contraceptives that are now available in Bulgaria.[3]

❖ The only emergency contraceptive available in Bulgaria is Postinor; this is a four-pill package given to women who do not have sexual intercourse on a regular basis.[4]

❖ Over a 20-year period, there have been remarkable changes in contraceptive use: Among married women aged 15–44, use of modern contraceptive methods increased from 6% in 1976 to 46% in 1995, while their reliance on traditional methods decreased from 70% to 40%. The proportion of women using no method decreased from 25% in 1976 to 14% in 1995. Although married women under the age of 20 did not increase their practice of contraception as much as women aged 20–44, their reliance on modern methods increased from 1% in 1976 to 18% in 1995.[5]

Abortion

❖ The abortion rate in Bulgaria is one of the highest in Europe, only falling behind the Soviet Union and Romania.[3]

❖ According to the law of 1956 every woman has a right to an abortion. This was updated in 1992 allowing abortions up to the 12th week of pregnancy. After the 12th week they are only allowed for a medical condition.[3]

❖ High abortion rates are due to lack of sex education and unavailability of contraceptives.[3]

❖ The religion in Bulgaria which is Eastern Orthodox does not oppose the woman's right to voluntary abortions as other religions in Europe do.[3]

❖ Over a 20-year period (1976 to 1995), an increasing share of pregnancies ended in abortion, while live births declined in relative frequency. In 1976, 49% of all pregnancies ended in abortion; by 1995, the proportion had increased to 57%.[5]

❖ Bulgaria's health service covers medically necessary abortions, as well as abortions for minors, women older than 35, women with an income below a specified level, and women whose pregnancy is a result of rape.[6]

Sex Education[1]

❖ There is a lack in sex education, which has led to an increase in teenage pregnancy.

❖ There is little opposition from the Orthodox Church regarding sex education or birth control.

Sexually Transmitted Infections (including HIV)[7]

❖ AIDS first appeared in Bulgaria in 1987.

❖ As of 2004, Bulgaria had reported a cumulative total of 471 cases of HIV infection acquired primarily through heterosexual transmission.

❖ HIV testing is mandatory among blood donations and systematic among many subgroups of the population. Since 1992 HIV testing is voluntary for pregnant women, STI patients and IDU in treatment centers.

- All foreign citizens who enter Bulgaria for more than 3 months must undergo testing.
- Diagnosed HIV infected cases are recorded in a national HIV database.
- The incidence of syphilis has been in the range of 20–30 per 100,000.

Sexual Orientation[8]

- The age of consent for homosexual activity is 18 (for heterosexuals it is 14 years).
- The Bulgarian Penal Code prohibits "scandalous homosexuality," homosexuality in public, and activities which may "lead to perversion." Violation of these laws can be punished with 1–5 years imprisonment and/or "social disgrace."
- Homosexuality has been a target for censorship in Bulgaria, as part of a government campaign for morality in television.

- On July 25th 1995, Ivan Granitshi, chief of the Bulgarian State Television said that programs featuring homosexuality will be taken off the air.

Prostitution[9]

- Prostitution itself is legal, but most activities around it (such as pimping) are outlawed.

Pornography[10]

- Hardcore pornographic material is "not recommended" for distribution to persons under the age of 18. Softcore material is rarely censored, even by the state TV stations. Magazines and pornographic papers have become increasingly available since the fall of communism in the early 1990s. Due to the unstable economy, by the late 1990s only a few publishers remain.

Resource

▶ Bulgarian Family Planning and Sexual Health Association (BFPA), 67 Knyaz Dondukov Boulevard, 1504 Sofia, Bulgaria. Tel: 359 (2) 943 30 52.

CANADA

Major Cities:	Toronto, Montreal, Vancouver, Ottawa, Edmonton
Ethnic Groups:	British Isles 28%; French 23%; other European 15%; Amerindian 2%; other (Asian, African, Arab) 6%
Languages:	English (official) 59% and French (official) 23%
Major Religions:	Roman Catholic 43%, Protestant 23% (United Church 10%, Anglican 7%, Baptist 2%, Lutheran 2%)
GDP per capita (PPP):	$34,000
Urban Population:	77%
Infant Mortality:	5 per 1,000 births
Life Expectancy:	Females: 84 years; Males: 77 years
Adult Literacy:	97%
Health Care System:	National health care system; 1 doctor per 455 persons.

References
❑ *The World Almanac and Book of Facts* (2006). NY: World Almanac Education Group.
❑ *The World Factbook* http://www.cia.gov/cia/publications/factbook/ Accessed June 25, 2006.
❑ *World Reference Atlas* (2005). NY: Dorling Kindersley Publishing.

Sexual Activity

❖ Age of consent is 14 years old for hetero-sexual and lesbian sex, and 18 years old for gay male sex. Put another way: age of consent for vaginal sex is 14, while anal sex is 18.[1]

❖ Half of Canadian students are sexually active by Grade 11.[2]

Contraception

❖ Those communities in Ontario where teenagers have access to clinical services for contraception along with sexuality education have lower rates of teen pregnancy.[2]

❖ According to the Ortho-McNeil survey, the most popular method of birth control for adolescent women is the Pill (22%), used either on its own (9%) or with a condom (13%). Only 5% of sexually active teens were not using any form of birth control.[3]

❖ Parental notification: The age at which it is thought that a person is capable of making his/her own decisions varies among the provinces from 14 to 18 years of age.[4]

❖ Emergency contraception is available. In 2005, Canada's national health agency, Health Canada, has approved emergency contraception (EC) Plan B for use without a doctor's prescription, allowing the pills to be sold at pharmacies nationwide.[5]

Abortion

❖ More than 70,000 pregnancies, or about 19% of all known pregnancies are terminated annually in Canada. Two-thirds occur among young, single women.[6]

❖ Almost 90% of abortions are performed in the first trimester (first 12 weeks) of pregnancy.[6]

❖ Legislation: Abortion is legal throughout the pregnancy.[7]

❖ The major issue involving abortion in Canada is access. Access is limited by geography and by attitudes of a minority.[8]

❖ Cost: Hospital abortions are covered by the national health system.[8]

❖ Chemical abortion is available in Canada on a limited basis using methotrexate and misoprostol; mifepristone (more widely known as RU-486) is not legally approved, and importation of that drug in Canada is currently illegal.[9]

Sex Education

❖ In most provinces, the law permits each regional school board to set its own guidelines.[10]

❖ Studies such as the Canada Youth and AIDS Study, which found that most teens were sexually active and most did not use condoms, prompted schools to improve their sexuality education programs as well as to install condom vending machines in secondary schools.[11]

Sexually Transmitted Infections (including HIV)[12]

❖ About 58,000 people were living with HIV/AIDS in Canada at the end of 2005.

❖ Information on HIV prevalence among pregnant women is available since 1989. HIV prevalence studies among pregnant women indicate an overall rate for Canada of between 3 and 5 per 10,000.

❖ Between 1996 and 2002, the estimated proportion of new infections that occurred among injecting drug users (IDUs) decreased from 47% to 30% while the proportion among men who have sex with men (MSM) increased from 30% to 40%. The proportion of new infections attributed to heterosexual transmission increased from 17% to 24% during this time period.

❖ Recent prevalence data on men who have sex with men (MSM) in Canada is limited; prevalence was about 25–36% in MSM in major urban areas during the mid-1980's and self-reported prevalence was 18–27% in the early 1990's. Incidence rate from MSM cohort studies in major urban areas was about 1–2% during 1995–98.

Sexual Orientation

❖ The Canadian Human Rights Act forbids discrimination based on sexual orientation by federally-regulated employers, landlords and services. The law applies to the federal government, banks, broadcasters, the phone and telecommunications industry, railways, airlines, and shipping and inter-provincial transportation. Federal constitutional protections are provided by the Canadian Charter of Rights and Freedoms. Provincial human rights laws provide protection based on sexual orientation in all Canadian provinces except Alberta, Newfoundland, and Prince Edward Island.[13]

❖ Canada lifted their ban on gays in the military in October 1992 after a lesbian lieutenant sued the military for discrimination.[14]

❖ In 2003 the provinces of Ontario and British Columbia granted full equal marriage rights to same-sex couples. Same-sex marriage was legalized across Canada by the Civil Marriage Act enacted in 2005 (the 4th country in the world).[15]

Prostitution[16]

❖ Prostitution is legal; pimping and public solicitation are illegal.

Pornography

❖ The Canadian criminal law provides that any publication that has as its "dominant characteristic" the "undue exploitation of sex" is obscene. Offenders are usually fined rather than jailed, and the law does not cover those who keep such material for personal use.[17]

❖ In *Butler v Her Majesty the Queen* (1992) involving the owner of a Manitoba sex shop, the court ruled that although the obscenity law infringed on freedom of expression, it was legitimate to outlaw pornography that was harmful to women. The court also redefined obscenity as sexually explicit material that involves violence or degradation.[18]

❖ Criminal code 163.1 makes it illegal to possess, produce, distribute or import child pornography (this includes depictions of youths under 18 and those who look as though they are under 18).[1]

❖ In Canada, it is illegal to communicate with a child over the Internet for the purpose of committing a sexual offence against that child (defined as "Internet luring").[19]

❖ In May 2004, the Government of Canada announced the National Strategy to Protect Children from Sexual Exploitation on the Internet. Under the strategy, the Government dedicated 43 million Canadian dollars over five years to ensure a comprehensive, coordinated approach to protect children on the Internet, and to pursue abusers.[19]

Resources

▶ Planned Parenthood Federation of Canada, 1 Nicholas Street, Suite 430, Ottawa, Canada K1N 7B7. Tel: 613-241-4474. Website: *http://www.ppfc.ca*

▶ Sex Information and Education Council of Canada (SEICAN), 850 Coxwell Avenue, East York, Ontario M4C 5RI Canada. Tel: 416–466-5304.

CHILE

CHILE
POPULATION: 16,134,219

CAPITAL: SANTIAGO
POPULATION: 5,333,100

Major Cities:	Santiago, Concepcion, Vinademeyer
Ethnic Groups:	White and White-Amerindian 95%; Amerindian 3%
Languages:	Spanish (official)
Major Religions:	Roman Catholic 89%, Protestant 11%
GDP per capita (PPP):	$11,300
Urban Population:	85%
Infant Mortality:	9 per 1,000 births
Life Expectancy:	Females: 80 years; Males: 73 years
Adult Literacy:	95%
Health Care System:	1 physician per 2,150 persons; health care is government responsibility.

References
❑ *The World Almanac and Book of Facts* (2006). NY: World Almanac Education Group.
❑ *The World Factbook* *http://www.cia.gov/cia/publications/factbook/* Accessed June 25, 2006.
❑ *World Reference Atlas* (2005). NY: Dorling Kindersley Publishing.

Sexual Activity

❖ Age of consent is 12 in heterosexual relations, 18 in homosexual.[1]
❖ 35% of all females, and 65% of all males have had premarital intercourse.[2]
❖ 70% of first births are conceived out-of-wedlock.[2]

Contraception[3]

❖ One-third of women of childbearing age use some type of contraceptive method. Of these women, 55.6% live in urban areas and 53.6% in rural areas.
❖ Contraceptive coverage through the public health care system reaches only 20% of women of childbearing age. Other private institutions meet the demand for contraceptives for the remaining contraceptive users.
❖ The contraceptives supplied by the public system include oral hormonal contraceptives, intrauterine devices (copper T), and to a lesser extent condoms, which are provided preferentially to high-risk groups. This restricted supply limits women's choices in controlling their fertility.
❖ Administrative pronouncements state that the legal age range for obtaining contraceptives is 15 to 44, but in reality the public health care system provides contraceptives only after the first pregnancy. This retroactive approach limits effective access of women of childbearing age to information and services that would enable them to exercise their reproductive rights.
❖ Women can now opt for voluntary sterilization, which is classified in the Responsible Parenthood Norms of the Ministry of Health as an irreversible contraceptive method. Women are required to meet the following conditions in order to be sterilized: they must have four living children, they must be at least 32 years old, and they must obtain the consent of their partner.

❖ The government has direct support of Emergency Contraception, and it is only available in emergencies.

Abortion

❖ Abortion is a criminal offense, in 1989 the government made a law which prohibits abortion (Law No. 18,826).[4]
❖ Anyone who performs an abortion may receive 3 years in prison.[4]
❖ Any woman inducing her own miscarriage may go to prison for 5 years.[4]
❖ It is estimated that approximately 160,000 abortions are performed each year, only some of which result in the woman seeking help at a hospital; it is also estimated that 35% of pregnancies end in abortion and that 40% of the women who have abortions are women under the age of 18.[3]
❖ Studies also show that one out of every three abortions requires hospitalization for serious complications, and that complications resulting from abortion represent approximately 30% of maternal deaths, constituting the primary cause of maternal mortality in Chile.[3]
❖ Poor women are most severely affected by the restrictive laws. Since they do not have the resources to obtain an abortion in safe conditions, they must resort to high-risk abortion methods that generally end in health complications or in death.[3]

Sex Education

❖ There are family planning services, and government supported programs, but since 1980 they have been less vocal in educating.[2]
❖ There is a lack of appropriate and sufficient sex education in schools.[2]
❖ Sex isn't a subject that's talked about between family members, or in schools.[2]

- Each year 40,000 children are born to teenage mothers, and in 18% of these cases the father is also an adolescent. Eighty percent of these pregnancies are unwanted, and the adolescents involved do not have the maturity to deal with the biological, psychological, social, and economic consequences. In 1996, 63.7% of the pregnancies to adolescents between the ages of 13 and 19 occurred among minors from rural areas. This reality is indicative of a deficient sex education curriculum with a biased treatment of sexuality that neither educates nor delivers information. This curriculum leaves young people exposed to early pregnancies, HIV-AIDS, other sexually transmissible infections (STIs), and clandestine abortions.[3]

- The only initiative taken in the area of sex education was promoted by the Commission for the Prevention of Adolescent Pregnancy, which initiated Community Days on Emotional and Sexual Life (JOCAS), beginning in 1996.[3]

- The scope of these efforts has been limited by opposition from conservative organizations and lack of government commitment. The JOCAS involve an educational dialogue between young people and adults on the emotional and sexual aspects of human life, and can be promoted by educational institutions or municipalities.[3]

- One of their successes is that they have opened a debate among various sectors on adolescent sexuality and have shown that adolescent sexual health is a social concern. However, there are obstacles in the form of a lack of institutional commitment to incorporating this issue at the policy level; the vocal opposition of conservative groups and the Catholic Church, which has been an obstacle to the development of commitment to this issue; and an academic culture that is resistant to educational innovations.[3]

Sexually Transmitted Infections (including HIV)[5]

- An estimated 26,000 people were living with HIV/AIDS in Chile at the end of 2004.

- More than half of the reported AIDS cases are due to men having sex with men and almost 30% were due to heterosexual transmission. Unlike other countries of the Southern Cone, injecting drug use does not appear to play a large role in HIV transmission in Chile. Heterosexual transmission is increasing in both men and women according to the official figures.

- HIV prevalence among 600 female sex workers receiving sexual health services at the Public Health System in Santiago was 0% in 2000.

Sexual Orientation[6]

- On December 23 1998, Chile's Official Daily of the Republic published Law 1047 which modifies the Penal Code, the Code for Criminal Procedures and Law 18216 regarding Punishment in Chile. The new legislation repealed the section that criminalized same sex sexual relations between consenting adults. Under the old provision homosexual relations between consenting adults could be punished with up to 5 years' imprisonment at the judge's discretion. The age of consent for same-sex activities was set at 18—higher than that for heterosexual activity—under the new Article 365.

- The repeal of the sodomy law in Chile represents a great victory for the gay, lesbian, bisexual, and transgender communities in Chile. Local activists have been organizing in their fight to repeal this unjust law for years. The change comes as part of a general reform of sexual crimes in Chile and was the result of a reform begun by the executive branch and agreed to unanimously by both legislative chambers.

Prostitution[7]

❖ Prostitution is illegal in all parts of the country.

Pornography[8]

❖ In January 2004, Chile amended its Penal Code to strengthen provisions dealing with sexual offenses committed against minors. The newly enacted law adds provisions to the code that prohibit the use of children in pornography and in the sale and distribution of materials containing child pornography, including through electronic means.

Resources

▶ Asociacion Chilena de Proteccion de la Familia (APROFA), Pérez Valenzuela 1098, Oficina 41, Providencia, Casilla 16504, Correo 9, Santiago 7530087 Chile. Tel: (56-2) 235-1435. Website: *http://www.aprofa.cl/*

▶ International Planned Parenthood Federation-Western Hemisphere Region (IPPF/WHR), 902 Broadway, tenth floor, New York, NY 10010.

▶ Latin American Population Program, Centro de Estudios de Poblacion (CENEP) Casilla 4398, Correo Central, 1000 Buenos Aires.

CHINA

Major Cities:	Shanghai, Peking (Beijing), Tianjin
Ethnic Groups:	Han Chinese 92%, Tibetan, Mongol, Korean, Manchu
Languages:	Standard Chinese or Mandarin (official); Yue, Wu, Hakka, Xiang, Gan, Minbel, Minnan, others
Major Religions:	Daoist (Taoist), Buddhist, Christians, some Muslim
GDP per capita (PPP):	$6,800
Urban Population:	32%
Infant Mortality:	28 per 1,000 live births
Life Expectancy:	Females: 75 years; Males: 71 years
Adult Literacy:	69%
Health Care System:	Three-tier network, made up of county hospitals, township health centers and village health stations, Barefoot Doctors program; 1 doctor for 1,060 people.

References

- *The World Almanac and Book of Facts* (2006). NY: World Almanac Education Group.
- *The World Factbook* *http://www.cia.gov/cia/publications/factbook/* Accessed June 25, 2006.
- *World Reference Atlas* (2005). NY: Dorling Kindersley Publishing.

Sexual Activity

* Legal age of consent is 14 for heterosexual relations.[1]
* China places a high value on female virginity. It is an important social norm, which controls the behavior of women.[2]
* Women are regarded as possessions, sex objects, and reproductive tools; in a society such as this sex becomes a commodity.[2]
* China denounces premarital sex, but sexual activity prior to marriage has become more common.[3]
* Sexual activity between men and women not involving intercourse is widely practiced and accepted.[3]
* Sex was primarily seen for procreation, but women are now looking for sexual fulfillment and pleasure from sex.[3]
* Older generations see sexual freedom as a threat to social stability.[4]
* Sexual dissatisfaction is a major cause of China's growing divorce rate.[4]
* Chinese population lacks knowledge about sex in general and about women's sexual needs.[5]
* Lack of privacy is one reason for sexual repression. Only 13% of married couples have ever made love in the nude.[6]

Contraception

* In 1979 China established a one-child family policy.[7]
* Curbing population growth is a national priority. Although a formal national family planning law does not exist, support for family planning is firmly embedded and codified in national and provincial laws and regulations.[8]
* The Constitution affirms the importance of family planning to curb population growth. Article 25 states that the People's Republic of China (PRC) "promotes family planning" as a necessary part of development. Article 49, which grants state protection to marriage and family, confirms the "duty" of both wife and husband to "practice family planning." Proclaimed as a "fundamental" national policy, the PRC's family planning policy has two basic goals: "control of population" and "improving the quality of the population.[8]
* The Marriage Law of 1980 (the "Marriage Law") requires family planning to be practiced. The law also promotes late marriage and late childbirth and sets the minimum age of marriage at 22 years of age for men and 20 years for women.[8]
* The Women's Protection Law recognizes that "women enjoy the freedom of choosing not to bear children."[8]
* Intrauterine devices ("IUDs") and sterilization are the most commonly used forms of contraception. Rates of use range from 41% for IUDs, 37% for tubal ligation, 12% for vasectomies, 5% for oral pills, 4% for condoms, 1% for spermicides, and 1% for other methods.[8]
* In 1992, while more than 156.6 million Chinese women were either sterilized or using IUDs, 31.7 million Chinese men were resorting to sterilizations and condoms.[8]

Abortion

* There are approximately 632 abortions for every 1,000 births.[8]
* The drug RU486 was approved for use in September 1989.[9]
* Official number of abortions performed annually in China is 10 million.[10]
* China's law on Maternal and Infant Health Care requires expectant mothers to undergo prenatal exams and to abort any fetus that shows abnormalities. Because these children neither maintain the family line nor support aging parents, they are considered a "luxury."[11]

- Doctors are permitted to veto the birth of any fetus they find abnormal or prone to genetic disease.[11]
- China forbids couples carrying a serious genetic disease to have children under the family law.[12]

Sex Education

- China seems to be changing its focus from procreation to pleasure. Books, videos and movies about human sexuality are becoming more available and there is a government awareness of the need to educate young people about there bodies and sexual desire.[3]
- China's first course in sex education started in 1988 at the Peoples' University.[4]
- People still rely on pornography and approved marriage manuals for sex information.[4]

Sexually Transmitted Infections (including HIV)

- HIV/AIDS was first reported in China in 1985.[13]
- China, with a fifth of the world's population, reported approximately 650,000 people were living with HIV in 2005. Injecting drug users account for almost half (44%) of people living with HIV. Almost one-half of China's injecting drug users share needles and syringes, and one in ten also engage in high-risk sexual behavior.[14]
- Since the early 1990s, tens of thousands of rural villagers have become infected through unsafe blood-donation procedures.[14]
- The percentage of female prostitutes who do not use condoms decreased from 67% in 1999, 49% in 2000 to 37% in 2001 (median).[13]
- In 1964 China declared itself free of venereal diseases, and research institutes for venereal diseases were closed.

However by 1990, research institutes on venereal diseases were reopened.[15]

- Rates of STI in China have soared over the past decade. Syphilis increased 20 times from 1990 to 1998 and the incidence of gonorrhea nearly tripled. The proportion of STIs acquired outside of marriage increased significantly (from 55% in 1995 to 72% in 1998.[16]
- Reported STIs rose from 430,000 cases in 1997 to 860,000 cases in 2000, suggesting that unprotected sex with non-monogamous partners is growing in China.[14]

Sexual Orientation[17]

- The topic of homosexuality had remained a taboo till the "open-door" policy was adopted around 1980. Before then, especially during the Great Cultural Revolution, gays and lesbians were subject to public criticism, sentenced to jail or administrative punishment. Even though gays, lesbians and other sexual minorities are still faced with harassment from the police and repression from the government, pressure of this kind is decreasing. Many gays and lesbians are asking for understanding from their parents and friends, coming out of traditional heterosexual marriages and ultimately, fighting for and defending their rights.
- The nineties became the "coming-out" time for gays and lesbians in China. At the same time, the government and the society became more tolerant for sexual minorities.
- In 1992, a social event for homosexuals called "Men's World" was held in Beijing. Both the government and the media showed their support.
- In 1993, with conservatism taking control of the ideology, any work in support of gay rights or public education regarding homosexuality was repressed.

❖ Although the law does not explicitly state whether homosexual behavior is legal or illegal, there is no law protecting the rights of gays and lesbians. The government is not very clear to the public. Under these circumstances, homosexuals have no place to claim their rights even when they are raided by criminals, fired from their workplace, kicked out of their homes and sent to mental institutions, etc. Many gays do not dare to speak about their situations for fear of the consequent humiliation and possible persecution.

❖ In 1994 the Chinese Psychiatric Association (CPA) passed the latest Chinese Classification of Mental Disorders (CCMD) in which homosexuality is still listed as a type of mental disorder. Many homosexuals are still forced to receive therapy or medication for "correcting" their sexual orientation.

Prostitution[15]

❖ In 1991 prostitution was prohibited in China.

❖ Forced re-education is punishment for prostitutes and Johns, which includes legal and moral education and manual labor in a specified camp. Time spent in these camps ranges from half a year to two years.

Pornography

❖ In November 1989 a campaign against pornographic activities and publications was introduced.[18] Because of harmful effects on society the campaign won universal support.[19]

❖ The resolution of pornography stipulates the death penalty or life imprisonment for serious cases of smuggling, producing, selling or distribution pornographic materials.[20]

❖ Belief that pornography is poison and it is changing the lives of young adults; studies show that students who view pornographic material slacken in their academic efforts and have less desire to be successful.[18] Pornographic materials are not available to people under 18, and is strictly punished.[20]

❖ Reference to homosexuality was deleted in new translations of Chinese classical literature. Chinese could no longer read the classics in uncensored form.[20]

❖ Books on anatomy and literary and art works containing sexually explicit material will not be considered pornographic materials.[20]

Resources

▶ China Association of Sex Education, Mercy Memorial Foundation, 11F, 171 Roosevelt Road, Section 3, Taipei Taiwan, R.O.C. Tel: 866-2-369-675.

▶ China Sexology Association, Number 38, Xue Yuan Lu, Haidion, Beijing 1000083.

▶ State Family Planning Commission, IEC Dept., 14 Zhichun Road, Haidian District, Beijing 100088.

COSTA RICA

COSTA RICA

POPULATION: 4,075,261

CAPITAL: SAN JOSE

POPULATION: 1,527,300

Major Cities:	San Jose, Alajuela, Cartago
Ethnic Groups:	White (including Mestizo) 94%, Black 3%
Languages:	Spanish (official), English
Major Religions:	Roman Catholic 76%, Evangelical 14%, Jehovah's Witness 2%
GDP per capita (PPP):	$11,100
Urban Population:	48%
Infant Mortality:	10 per 1,000 births
Life Expectancy:	Females: 80 years; Males: 74 years
Adult Literacy:	93%
Health Care:	1 doctor per 1,205 persons. 80% of the population has access to health services. Only 54% of the population has access to prenatal care.

References

❑ *The World Almanac and Book of Facts* (2006). NY: World Almanac Education Group.

❑ *The World Factbook* *http://www.cia.gov/cia/publications/factbook/* Accessed June 25, 2006.

❑ *World Reference Atlas* (2005). NY: Dorling Kindersley Publishing.

Sexual Activity

❖ Legal age of consent is 15 years old for both heterosexuals and homosexuals.[1]

❖ 59% of unmarried women ages 15–24 who became pregnant reported that the pregnancy was unintended.[2]

❖ The median age of first intercourse is 19.4 years for women and 17.4 years of age for men.[3]

Contraception

❖ 70% of women use some form of contraception.[4]

❖ More than three-quarters (77%) of women users of modern contraceptive methods acquire them, almost free of charge, from the government public services including the social security system, the Ministry of Health and company physicians. 28% of women use modern methods of contraception, 21% are sterilized and 16% use barrier methods. In metropolitan San José 61% of women users obtain their contraceptives in public health facilities, while 87% of women living in rural areas depend on this source.[5]

❖ Emergency contraception is not available in Costa Rica.[6]

Abortion[7]

❖ Abortion is legal only when maternal health is compromised.

Sex Education[8]

❖ Since August of 1998, the First Lady of Costa Rica was promoting the implementation of a national program of sex education for children and youth which would conform to "Christian values," (meaning it would not include discussions of such topics as gender, homosexuality, and contraception).

Sexually Transmitted Infections (including HIV)[9]

❖ An estimated 12,000 people were living with HIV/AIDS in Costa Rica at the end of 2003.

❖ The main mode of HIV transmission is men having sex with men which represents 68% of all AIDS reported cases in the country.

Sexual Orientation[10]

❖ Homosexuality is not acceptable in Costa Rica; there is a lot of discrimination against gays and lesbians.

❖ In a first of its kind decision, Costa Rica's "Defensoria de los Habitantes" [the government's human rights ombudsperson] has ruled that the Costa Rican government may not deny legal recognition to gays and other minorities. The "Registro Civil" of the government here considers applications for all legal charters. In the decision the Defensoria ruled that the original decision by the Registro Civil to deny legal recognition of Triangulo Rosa gay group, is in violation of the country's constitution which guarantees the right of association to all citizens. Decisions made by the Defensoria are legally binding.

Prostitution[1]

❖ Prostitution is legal in Costa Rica.

❖ Prostitutes must have an ID card and carry it at all times to prove it.

❖ Age of consent is 18.

Pornography

❖ No information found.

Resources

▶ Asociacion Demografica Costarricense (ADC), La Uruca Condominios Horizontales JW, Locales 26 y 27, contiguo al Banco Nacional · Apartado Postal 10203-1000, San José Costa Rica. Tel: (506) 258-7139. Website: *http://www.adc-cr.org/*

▶ Programa Salud Reproductiva, Apartado 1434-1011 Y-Griega, San Jose, Costa Rica.

CUBA

CUBA

POPULATION: 11,382,820

CAPITAL: **HAVANA**
POPULATION: 2,686,000

Major Cities:	Havana, Santiago, Camaguey
Ethnic Groups:	Mulatto 51%, White 37%, Black 11%
Languages:	Spanish (official)
Major Religions:	Roman Catholic 85% prior to Castro
GDP per capita (PPP):	$3,5000
Urban Population:	75%
Infant Mortality:	6 per 1,000 births
Life Expectancy:	Females: 80 years; Males: 75 years
Adult Literacy:	96%
Health Care System:	1 doctor per 333 persons.

References

❑ *The World Almanac and Book of Facts* (2006). NY: World Almanac Education Group.
❑ *The World Factbook* http://www.cia.gov/cia/publications/factbook/ Accessed June 25, 2006.
❑ *World Reference Atlas* (2005). NY: Dorling Kindersley Publishing.

Sexual Activity

❖ The legal age of consent is 16 for both heterosexuals and homosexuals.[1]

Contraception

❖ Contraception is widely available in Cuba in all government health centers, but contraception failure is high.[2]
❖ It is estimated that approximately 70 per cent of Cuban women of reproductive age are currently using a contraceptive method.[2]
❖ Cuba needs 160 million condoms a year, but can only afford 43 million.[3]

Abortion[2]

❖ Abortion has been legal in Cuba since the late 1960s.
❖ The pregnant woman must be examined by a gynecologist and must receive counseling from a social worker.
❖ If the woman is unmarried and under 16 years of age, parental permission is required.
❖ If gestation is greater than 10 weeks, authorization by health authorities is required.
❖ The abortion must be performed by a physician in an official health center.

Sex Education

❖ No information found.

Sexually Transmitted Infections (including HIV)

❖ At the end of 2005, Cuba had an adult HIV prevalence of 0.1%. There were an estimated 4,800 people living with HIV and less than 500 people died of AIDS-related illnesses.[4]
❖ The country's prevention of mother-to-child transmission of HIV program is among the most effective in the world and has kept the total number of babies born with HIV to date below 100. Cuba also offers free, universal access to anti-retroviral therapy, which has limited both the number of AIDS cases and AIDS deaths.[5]
❖ Cuba is the only country that imposes AIDS test on all its' people, and the only one that confines for life anyone carrying the HIV virus.[6]
❖ Cuba established an extensive HIV surveillance program in 1983, and more than 15 million HIV antibody test have been done. The sexual contacts of all infected persons are closely observed.[6]

Sexual Orientation[7]

❖ Homosexual behavior in the public sphere is illegal; there were 3–9 month fines for anyone who practices homosexual acts or makes public displays of homosexuality.
❖ Today life for gay people in Cuba is similar, in some sense, to life for gay people in the United States, however the homosexuality of many men and women is a matter of public record. It is the complete absence of a public sphere that most clearly distinguishes the life of homosexuals in Cuba from any corresponding lifestyle in the United States.
❖ There are no real gay meeting establishments, but private parties called "10 Pesos" (cost of admission). A system of "warnings" exists for Cuban gays who are identified at these places (a third written warning can mean a prison term). Nevertheless, despite such arbitrary police practice, in the last few years there has been a shift towards greater tolerance of gay parties and gatherings.
❖ Genuine freedom of association does not exist, as evidenced by the suppression of the Cuban Association of Gays and Lesbians in 1997.

Prostitution[8]

❖ Prostitution is illegal in Cuba, however the 40% rise in tourism in Cuba has spawned a resurgence of the nation's sex industry.

Pornography

❖ No information found.

Resources

▶ Centro Iberoamericano de Formacano Pedagogica y Orintacion Educational (CIFPOE), Calle 108. Number 29E08, entre 29 E y 29 F, Ciudad Escolar Libertad, Mariano, La Havana.

▶ Sociedad Cinetifica Cubana Para el Desarrollo de la Familia (SOCUDEF), 5ta Avenida 3207, Esquina 34, Miramar, Havana, Cuba.

CZECH REPUBLIC

CZECH REPUBLIC
POPULATION: 10,235,455

CAPITAL: **PRAGUE (PRAHA)**
POPULATION: 1,378,700

Major Cities:	Brno, Ostrava, Pilsen
Ethnic Groups:	Czech 90%, Moravian 3%, Slovak 2%
Languages:	Czech
Major Religions:	Roman Catholic 27%, Protestant 2%
GDP per capita (PPP):	$19,500
Urban Population:	75%
Infant Mortality:	4 per 1,000 births
Life Expectancy:	Females: 80 years, Males: 73 years
Adult Literacy:	99%
Health Care System:	Private practice encouraged, good insurance system, all activities directed by the Minister of Health, with attention to prevention. 1 doctor per 270 persons.

References
❑ *The World Almanac and Book of Facts* (2006). NY: World Almanac Education Group.
❑ *The World Factbook* http://www.cia.gov/cia/publications/factbook/ Accessed June 25, 2006.
❑ *World Reference Atlas* (2005). NY: Dorling Kindersley Publishing.

Sexual Activity[1]

❖ Age of consent for sexual activity is 15.[1]

❖ Since 1989 the Czech Republic has been experiencing a sexual revolution, development of a sex industry, and societal tendencies toward increased sexual activity.[2]

Contraception

❖ Until 1990, condoms were the only contraceptives that had to be paid for. However, the use of contraception was very low, with only 7.2 percent of women aged 15–44 using the pill, and only 16.9 percent using an IUD.[3]

❖ Until 1990, women were told that oral contraceptives and IUDs were hazardous to their health, and thus relied on abortions as birth control.[4]

❖ Today, only 28% of women at risk of unplanned pregnancy use modern contraceptives.[4]

❖ Under the new economic policy, consumers must pay for abortion and contraceptive supplies.[4]

❖ IUD insertion is covered by health insurance.[4]

❖ Oral contraceptives cost only 1–2% of an average monthly income.

❖ Since 1990, when women first had to pay for contraception, modern contraceptive method use has been *increasing*, according to growing sales of contraceptives.[4]

❖ Gynecologists view condoms as somewhat convenient, and only somewhat reliable against pregnancy and disease.[4]

❖ Only 65% of gynecologists think that abstinence is 100% reliable against unplanned pregnancy and sexually transmitted disease, and only 39% of them perceived this as a 'very safe' method. 5% viewed it as a convenient method.[4]

❖ 80% of gynecologists prescribe the Pill very often and 63% of them view it as 100% reliable, while only 25% of them perceive it to be 'very safe.' 90% believe that the Pill is very convenient.[4]

❖ Postinor, a post-coital contraceptive or "morning-after" pill, is registered in the Czech Republic.[5]

Abortion

❖ Abortion is available on request, with the consent of the woman and authorization by her gynecologist. After 12 weeks, abortion may be performed for medical reasons only.[6]

❖ Except for medical reasons, they must be performed during the first trimester in a hospital, by a licensed gynecologist.[6]

❖ Women under the age of 16 must have parental/guardian consent, and women between the ages of 16 and 18 must notify their parent/guardian.[6]

❖ 75% of abortions are performed using the vacuum aspiration method.[6]

❖ Legislation is becoming more and more liberal.[3]

❖ Termination of pregnancy for other than health reasons now can cost from 20–50% of the average monthly salary.[3]

❖ The number of abortions has slowly decreased since 1990's changes to the price system.[3]

Sex Education

❖ One of the priorities of the Czech Family Planning Association is to make sex education more effective.[3]

❖ Sex education is mainly taught as a part of biology, health or other science classes.[7]

❖ Family Life Education is also a specific course subject, where sex education is addressed.[7]

❖ The Czech Republic begins sex education with gender physical differences and roles. This is taught to younger children. Pre-adolescents are taught reproduction facts, including puberty and hygiene. Adolescents are taught biological facts, contraception, and AIDS and STD prevention.[7]

❖ The Czech Republic has a preventive model of sex education.[7]

❖ The Family Planning Association is the main agency involved with sex education. It provides teacher training, youth lectures, and it belongs to a sex education policy-making body, and provides advocacy.[7]

❖ Public climate towards sex education is moderate.[7]

Sexually Transmitted Infections (including HIV)

❖ An estimated 650 people were living with HIV/AIDS in the Czech Republic in 2004.[8]

❖ Estimated prevalence and incidence of HIV/AIDS is still relatively low and the epidemiological situation seems stable.[8]

❖ No HIV infection has been reported in blood donors since 1995.[8]

❖ Approximately 80% of all HIV cases are male, mainly homo and bisexual men, and only 5.4% were injecting drug users.[8]

❖ Two thirds of all HIV infections are among residents of the capital city Prague and its immediate vicinity.[8]

❖ Almost one quarter of all reported HIV cases were among foreign citizens.[8]

❖ Nearly 70% of all gonorrhea cases, and 50–60% of all new syphilis cases are found in the population group of 15 and 24 years of age.[2]

Sexual Orientation[9]

❖ The age of consent for homosexuals in the Czech Republic has been reduced to 15 (from 18), the same as for heterosexuals.

❖ Consensual homosexual behavior between adults was decriminalized in 1961.

❖ There are no antidiscrimination laws to protect gays and lesbians. . . a constitutional list of human rights and freedoms was accepted by the Czechoslovak Parliament in 1991 (Law 23/1991). Deputy Klara Samkova wanted "sexual orientation" to be added to the list, but this was not approved by the majority of Parliament.

❖ SOHO is the Czech abbreviation for their Association of Homosexual Citizen's Organizations, made up of about 20 organizations. Since 1995, SOHO has worked towards official registered homosexual partnerships in the Czech Republic, without any success.

Prostitution[2]

❖ July 11, 1990 abolished two penal laws concerning prostitution, since that date it is no longer considered a criminal offense.

❖ The high earnings associated with prostitution have made it an attractive occupation.

❖ Most prostitutes operate in the streets of large cities or on highways.

❖ Most prostitutes are less than 18 years of age and many started as young as 13 or 14 years old.

Pornography

❖ Since the fall of communism in 1989, Czech media lifted its ban on censorship, and pornography began to flourish.[10]

❖ Foreign publications, such as *Penthouse* and *Playboy* are popular, as well as those of the Czech Republic.[11]

Resources

▶ Czech Republic Family Planning Association: Spolecnost pro plánování rodiny a sexuální v?chovu (SPRSV), Senovazna 2, 111 21 Prague 1, Czech Republic. Tel: +420 (2) 242 315 24.

▶ Czechoslavak Sexological Society/Institute of Sexology, Charles University, Prague, Karlov Nam_sti 32, Prague 2, 120 00.

DENMARK

DENMARK
POPULATION: 5,450,661

CAPITAL: COPENHAGEN
POPULATION: 1,094,400

Major Cities:	Copenhagen, Arhus, Odense, Aalborg
Ethnic Groups:	Scandinavian, Inuit, Faroese, German, Turkish
Languages:	Danish, Faroese, Greenlandic
Major Religions:	Evangelical Lutheran 95%, other Protestant and Roman Catholic 3%
GDP per capita (PPP):	$34,600
Urban Population:	85%
Infant Mortality:	5 per 1,000 births
Life Expectancy:	Females: 80 years; Males: 75 years
Adult Literacy:	100%
Health Care System:	Doctors appointed by Health Security Service; few private clinics, mostly hospitals. 1 doctor per 357 persons.

References
❑ *The World Almanac and Book of Facts* (2006). NY: World Almanac Education Group.
❑ *The World Factbook* http://www.cia.gov/cia/publications/factbook/ Accessed June 25, 2006.
❑ *World Reference Atlas* (2005). NY: Dorling Kindersley Publishing.

Sexual Activity

❖ Age of consent is 15 years of age.[1]

❖ Denmark has a very liberal attitude towards teenage sexuality and has recognized the fact that young, unmarried women have a sexual life.[2]

❖ Teenage pregnancies are not too common. The number has been decreasing rapidly for the past 20 years. For example, only 12 children were born to mothers under 16 years of age in 1993. Most teenage pregnancies end with an abortion.[2]

❖ Seventy-one percent of young women surveyed said they began having sex before age 18.[3]

Contraception

❖ Parental consent is not needed for young people to acquire contraceptives. Denmark was the first country in the world to grant this right to youth in 1966.[2]

❖ In March 1991, the Family Planning Association launched a series of 10 pamphlets on different contraceptive methods which were distributed free of charge. By 1995, 150,000 copies had been distributed.[4]

❖ Emergency contraception: The most popular method of contraception is the morning after pill which is taken within 2–3 days of intercourse but is available in a strip of 21 pills only. In 1994, the total sales of the 21-pack were 14,000. In April 1995, the surgeon general ordered that a pack for emergency use should be available on prescription.[4]

Abortion

❖ Denmark has had free access to legal abortion since 1973 when a law passed that allowed women to have an abortion on demand during the first 12 weeks of pregnancy after the submission of an application and after being informed of the risks and alternatives. Abortion is available after 12 weeks when authorized by a committee of one social worker and two physicians. They would approve if one of many conditions applied.[5]

❖ The law states that a woman is "entitled" to undergo an abortion during the first 12 weeks. County hospital boards are responsible for providing services, and each county has at least one hospital with the capacity to perform abortions.[6]

❖ Minors must have written parental consent.[3]

❖ Abortion rates have dropped 40% since 1975.[7]

❖ RU 486 (mifepristone) became available in Denmark in 1999.[8]

Sex Education[2]

❖ Sex and social life education has been a compulsory subject in Danish schools since 1970 but has been a tradition long before then.

❖ The sex education curriculum focuses on medical and anatomical lessons, psychological and ethical aspects of sexual and couples' relations, love, sexuality, pregnancy, STD's, and abortion, homosexuality and knowledge about sexual minorities.

Sexually Transmitted Infections (including HIV)[9]

❖ An estimated 4,006 people were living with HIV/AIDS in Denmark in 2004.

❖ An anonymous HIV case reporting system was implemented in August 1990. Data collection includes information on risk behavior, previous testing and results and on nationality. The number of HIV tests conducted are reported monthly.

❖ No routine screening programs exist except for blood donors.

- Among Danish nationals the transmission is primarily among MSM, whereas for foreigners the transmission is primarily heterosexual. However among the Danish nationals an increasing proportion is largely due to a rise in cases diagnosed in heterosexuals with a partner originating from a country with a generalized HIV epidemic.

- Cross-sectional studies on knowledge, attitude and behavior among MSM have been conducted since 2000. The first results indicate that many of them were still practicing unsafe sex that may expose them to HIV. Such results may have great implications for prevention work.

- Out of the 265 new HIV infections in 2003, 164 were among Danish nationals, of those 146 were male and 18 were female. Among the 146 new HIV cases in Danish males 65% were among MSM, 27% were among heterosexuals, 7% were among IDUs and 1% was classified as others. Of the 18 new HIV cases in Danish females 61% were transmitted through heterosexual contact, 33% among IDUs and 6% in other ways.

- Incidence of syphilis has been fairly low for many years while the incidence of gonorrhea has decreased since mid-1980's. But there was a slight increase in the last few years, mainly among men.

- The annual incidence of chlamydia has not changed in recent years and is still relatively high; it is highest among young women age 20–24, with an annual incidence of around 2.2%.

Sexual Orientation

- The Danish Penal Code has an anti-discrimination clause dealing with sexual orientation. It includes public employment and the private labor market.[10]

- In 1989 Denmark became the first country in the world to introduce a registered partnership law. The law enabled two persons of the same sex to register their partnership and gave them (with some exceptions) the same rights and responsibilities as a heterosexual married couple.[10]

- In 1999, improvements were made to the registered partnership law:
  - citizens from Norway, Sweden and Iceland have the same rights as Danish citizens in relation to registered partnership.
  - citizens of other countries having similar legislation as the partnership law can get the same rights.
  - two non-Danish citizens can enter into registered partnership if both partners have stayed in Denmark for at least two years.
  - a partner in a registered partnership can adopt the children of her/his partner unless the child is adopted from a foreign country.

- The remaining differences between marriage and registered partnership are:
  - no insemination by public health services for lesbians
  - no adoption of foreign children
  - no possibility of church wedding, but blessings are possible
  - the two-years limit for foreigners.[11]

- Homosexuals are welcome in the armed forces of Denmark.[11]

Prostitution[2]

- Prostitution is not a criminal offense in Denmark. Neither the customer, nor the prostitute is committing an offense.

- Prostitution is considered criminal vagrancy if the woman has no other means of support.

Pornography

- A "porno wave" began in Denmark around 1964 but had receded by 1970 after pornography was legalized in the late 1960's.[12]

❖ In 1969 Denmark was the first country in the world to legalize hardcore pornography.[12]

❖ Possession of child pornography is a crime since 1994 as well as the sale and production of child pornography.[2]

Resources

▶ Danish Association for Clinical Sexology (DACS), Kuhlausgade 46, DK-2100, Copenhagen. Tel: 45/392-92399. Fax: 45/354-57684.

▶ Danish Family Planning Association, Foreningen Sex & Samfund, Rosenørns Allé 12, 1634 Copenhagen V, Denmark. Tel: 45 (33) 931 010. Website: *http://www.sexogsamfund.dk/*

EGYPT

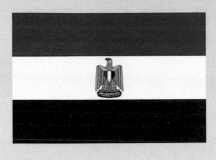

Major Cities:	Cairo, Alexandria, Giza
Ethnic Groups:	Egyptians 98%, Berbers, Nubian, and Bedouins 1%
Languages:	Arabic (official), English, French
Major Religions:	Muslim (mostly Sunni) 90%, Coptic 9%
GDP per capita (PPP):	$3,900
Urban Population:	45%
Infant Mortality:	31 per 1,000 births
Life Expectancy:	Females: 74 years; Males: 69 years
Adult Literacy:	58%
Health Care System:	Free health service provided by government; fee-for-service by private physicians; 1 doctor per 1,340 persons.

References

❑ *The World Almanac and Book of Facts* (2006). NY: World Almanac Education Group.
❑ *The World Factbook* *http://www.cia.gov/cia/publications/factbook/* Accessed June 25, 2006.
❑ *World Reference Atlas* (2005). NY: Dorling Kindersley Publishing.

Sexual Activity

❖ Age of consent is 18.[1]

❖ Interaction between the sexes is extremely limited prior to marriage; marriage is difficult because it is very expensive; it is unacceptable to live together unless married.[2]

❖ Dating is viewed with disapproval in this society where arranged marriages are prevalent.[2]

❖ More than 90% of Egyptian girls undergo a surgical "female circumcision" (FC/FGM) to control or prevent sexual intercourse.[3] About 2 million girls per year are subjected to female genital mutilation, largely through parental consent and custom.[4]

❖ In 1994, the Egyptian government pledged at the U.N. Population Conference to outlaw female circumcision entirely. They first issued a decree banning FC/FGM outside of public hospitals and required physicians to discourage parents from having their daughters undergo FC/FGM. If the parents insisted, the procedure was to be carried out by physicians in hospitals.[5]

❖ In 1995, Dr. Abdel Fattah, the former Minister of Health, issued a decree amending the 1994 policy on FC/FGM. Using the rationale that Egyptian parents had been successfully convinced to eschew the practice of FC/FGM, the 1995 decree banned physicians from performing FC/FGM in public hospitals. However, this decree did not prevent physicians from performing FC/FGM in their private clinics. In 1996 the new Minister of Health, Dr. Ismael Sallam, ended this policy with a decree prohibiting FC/FGM in public hospitals and private clinics, as well as by non-physicians.[5]

❖ Shortly after the 1996 decree was issued, it was challenged in court by proponents of FC/FGM and by medical professionals concerned that the ban would lead to increased clandestine FC/FGM. The court declared the health minister's decree unconstitutional for infringing upon parliamentary functions and for interfering with the right of physicians to perform surgery. However, in December 1997, the highest court overturned the lower court's ruling and, in response to proponents of FC/FGM who asserted that Islam requires the practice, declared that Islam does not sanction FC/FGM. The court also declared the practice punishable under the Penal Code.[5]

❖ Other efforts of the Egyptian government to eliminate FC/FGM include educating traditional birth attendants, doctors, and nurses about the dangers of FC/FGM, and developing mass-media public service messages that discourage FC/FGM.[5]

Contraception

❖ Egyptian Family Planning Association has been providing services since 1958. Egypt is a leader in family planning in the Middle East, a region where contraceptive use is relatively low.[6]

❖ According to one survey of 10,000 households, about 30% of married women, 30% of single women, and 5% of previously married women were using contraception. Of those married women using contraception, 30% were using IUDs and 13% were using the pill.[7]

❖ Emergency contraception is not yet available.[8]

Abortion

❖ Abortion in Egypt is illegal. The Egyptian penal code of 1937 prohibits abortion in all circumstances but under criminal law, abortion is permitted to save the life of the pregnant woman; the husband's consent is required.[9]

❖ Anyone who induces an abortion is subject to imprisonment.[9]

- More recently, different approaches are taken on abortion, ranging from complete prohibition (the Maliki sect) to complete permission (the Zaydi sect). As a result of conflicting legal status and differing theological opinions, the availability of safe abortion services is limited in Egypt.[10]
- MIFEPRISTONE/RU 486 (non-surgical "abortion pill"): Not available in Egypt.[11]

Sex Education[2]

- Open discussion of sexuality is socially unacceptable; Egypt uses an approach that emphasizes repression rather than education.

Sexually Transmitted Infections (including HIV)[12]

- An estimated 12,000 people were living with HIV/AIDS in Egypt at the end of 2003.
- In Egypt, there appears to be a small amount of AIDS awareness. AIDS cases are either rare or covered up; safe sex practices are virtually unknown.
- A small number of sex workers, MSM and drug users have been tested yearly and the rate of HIV infection remains very low.
- Egypt has consistently low HIV prevalence rates, based on reported data from the National AIDS Program. The mode of transmission among cases reported through June 2001 was: 45% heterosexual, 21% men who have sex with men (MSM), 6% injection drug use (IDU), 16% via blood products, < 1% mother to child transmission (MTCT), and 11% due to unknown causes.
- Access to groups with known behavioral risk for HIV, such as MSM, sex workers, and especially drug users, is difficult in Egypt due to cultural constraints.

Sexual Orientation

- There is a strong social sanction against all openly gay or lesbian life. Homosexuality is taboo but very common (more so among men).[2]
- Men have traditionally had sex with other men until marriage and sometimes after that, but it's discreet. Lesbianism is also common but discreet.[2]
- There are no official gay organizations or gay bars but a few hammams-Turkish baths for men.[2]
- Homosexuality is not mentioned in the law. Egypt has some regulations concerning "offences against public morals and sensitivities" which could be used against homosexuals, but technically same-sex relations are legal.[13]
- Egypt has no exclusive military policies regarding homosexual behavior.[13]

Prostitution[14]

- Prostitution is illegal.

Pornography[15]

- Censorship: No video or record album may be legally sold until it is scrutinized by a government censor to ensure that the work adheres to the countries "specific moral standards."

Resources

- Alexandria Model Family Planning Clinic, 17, Sidi El-Metwally Street, El-Attarien, Alexandria, 4933867. Tel: 20-3/493-3867.

- Egyptian Family Planning Association, 6 Gazirat El Arab Street, Al Mohandissen, El Giza, Cairo. Tel: 20-2/360-7329.

FINLAND

FINLAND

POPULATION: 5,231,372

CAPITAL: HELSINKI

POPULATION: 1,162,900

Major Cities:	Helsinki, Espoo, Tamere
Ethnic Groups:	Finns 94%; Swedes 6%
Languages:	Finnish (official) 92%, Swedish (official) 6%
Major Religions:	Lutheran National Church 84%
GDP per capita (PPP):	$23,780
Urban Population:	67%
Infant Mortality:	4 per 1,000 births
Life Expectancy:	Females: 82 years; Males: 75 years
Adult Literacy:	100%
Health Care System:	Physicians: 1 per 385 persons.

References

❑ *The World Almanac and Book of Facts* (2006). NY: World Almanac Education Group.
❑ *The World Factbook* http://www.cia.gov/cia/publications/factbook/ Accessed June 25, 2006.
❑ *World Reference Atlas* (2005). NY: Dorling Kindersley Publishing.

Sexual Activity

❖ The age of consent is 16 for heterosexual and homosexual relations.[1]
❖ Half of young women said they began having sex before age 18.[2]
❖ There are no signs of increasing sexual activity among adolescents, despite rigorous sex education in the schools and mass media.[3]

Contraception

❖ In 1972 legislation added an entry into force of the Primary Health Care Act. The law ordered that every local municipality must have a health centre which provides primary health care services for its inhabitants, including contraceptive counseling.[3]
❖ A visit to the family planning clinic and the first contraceptive method (for instance oral contraceptives for 3–6 months) are free of charge. The services are funded by local municipalities with the support of government subsidies, the most common being the Family Federation of Finland, which has clinics in most of the larger towns of the country and a youth center in Helsinki.[3]
❖ Adolescents can also resort to school health services, which offer advice in sexual and contraceptive problems.[3]
❖ The services are free of charge and in larger cities and communities the services are concentrated in family planning clinics.[4]
❖ Emergency Contraception (also called "post-coital" birth control): Obtained from the family planning centers or a pharmacy with a prescription, and has been available since the mid 1980s. Although use is impossible to estimate, the sales figures of the special post-coital contraception package show an increasing trend.[4]

Abortion

❖ Legislation: In 1970 passed a much broader law than previously which includes sufficient social grounds for abortion. In 1979 a restriction was included in the law according to which an abortion induced on social grounds must be performed during the first 12 weeks of pregnancy. The law forbids abortion after the 16th week of pregnancy except on medical grounds, in which case there is no limitation, and abortion may be granted up to the 24th week on eugenic grounds.[5]
❖ It is estimated that the number of illegal abortions in the 1950s and 1960s varied between 18,000 and 25,000 annually. Under present law they have disappeared almost totally.[5]
❖ An indication that abortion has not become a birth control method in Finland is that the majority of abortions induced annually are first ones.[5]
❖ Under current law, access to abortions services is fairly equal throughout Finland.[5]
❖ Minors need consent from parents, and the cost is free of charge if performed in a public hospital.[6]
❖ Abortion rates have declined by over 50% since 1975. Education and access to services have played a major role in reducing unplanned pregnancy.[7]
❖ RU-486 (Mifepristone) was approved for marketing in 1999.[8]

Sex Education[3]

❖ The need for more effective sex education among teenagers was recognized at the preparatory stage of the present abortion law, and sex education was integrated into the curriculum in 1970.
❖ Currently, sex education in Finland begins at age 11 on changes in puberty and advances from there on according to

the children's developmental stage. By the age of 16 all adolescents should have learned about both the physiology of reproduction and methods of contraception.

❖ The Finnish program against HIV has one feature which is probably unique in the world; every year since 1987 the national health authorities have mailed an illustrated magazine to all adolescents who will be 16 that year containing information on the prevention of HIV and other STDs, as well as on sexual issues in general. The package also contains a condom and a letter to the parents. Public response to this campaign has been mainly positive, and it has probably contributed to the increased knowledge of sexual issues among teenagers.

Sexually Transmitted Infections (including HIV)

❖ Since the start of the epidemic and as of December 2003, 1,625 persons had been diagnosed with HIV. Of these 75% are men and 25% women. Foreigners contribute 26% of all reported HIV cases. Of those cases with a reported mode of transmission (1,427), the majority are heterosexual (40%) or homo/bi-sexual cases (20%). A further 20% are drug injectors.[9]

❖ The majority of heterosexual cases (60%) are cases from countries with generalized HIV epidemics and a further 7% of heterosexual cases are cases with sexual partners from countries with generalized epidemics.[9]

❖ Annual incidence of new HIV cases had been relatively low and stable, with a small peak in 1992 when 93 new cases were reported, declining to 69 cases in 1996.[9]

❖ The low rate of STIs in Finland can be attributed to the high quality of diagnostic and treatment methods, the free or

low cost of these services, the guarantee of confidentiality provided by clinics, and a high rate of condom use. Because there is less stigma of having an STI in Finland and treatment is free or low cost, barriers to treatment and greater spread of STIs are also reduced.[10]

Sexual Orientation

❖ Legislation: In Finland the law prohibiting homosexual relations was repealed in 1971. Before that relations between women and relations between men were both illegal. Homosexuality was removed from the official classification of diseases in 1981.[11]

❖ The Finnish Penal Code protects individuals from discrimination based on their sexual orientation in terms of public or commercial services or access to public meetings. The law also prohibits discrimination in hiring and working conditions.[11]

❖ In June 1998 the Finnish Parliament swept away the two provisions of the criminal law which still discriminated against lesbians and gays: the age of consent was equalized, and the law banning the "public encouragement or incitement of unchastity between members of the same sex" (Article 20.9.2) was repealed.[11]

❖ Same-sex couples have been treated as common-law couples when the wording of the law allows it. There is no procedure or custom other than marriage whereby a partnership (be it heterosexual or homosexual) can be registered.[11]

❖ There is no discrimination of homosexuals in the military.[12]

Prostitution[13]

❖ Prostitution is neither illegal nor regulated.

❖ Pimping and promoting prostitution are forbidden.

Pornography[14]

❖ Child, snuff and bestiality pornography is banned. It's allowed to sell pornography in every store, but magazines to buyers of 15 years or older and hardcore to buyers of 18 years or older.

Resource

▶ Finland Family Planning Association: Väestöliitto, Iso Roobertinkatu 20-22A, 00100, Helsinki. Tel: 358 (9) 228 050. Website: *http://www.vaestoliitto.fi/*

FRANCE

FRANCE

POPULATION: 60,876,136

CAPITAL: **PARIS**

POPULATION: 9,854,000

Major Cities:	Paris, Lyon, Marseilles, Lillie
Ethnic Groups:	Celtic and Latin, with Teutonic, Slavic, North African, Indochinese, Basque minorities
Languages:	French (official)
Major Religions:	Roman Catholic 83–88%
GDP per capita (PPP):	$29,900
Urban Population:	75%
Infant Mortality Rate:	4 per 1,000 births
Life Expectancy at Birth:	Females: 84 years; Males: 76 years
Literacy:	99%
Health Care System:	National health care available; 1 doctor per 357 persons.

References

❏ *The World Almanac and Book of Facts* (2006). NY: World Almanac Education Group.
❏ *The World Factbook* http://www.cia.gov/cia/publications/factbook/ Accessed June 25, 2006.
❏ *World Reference Atlas* (2005). NY: Dorling Kindersley Publishing.

Sexual Activity

* Age of consent for heterosexual and homosexual relations is 15 years of age.[1]
* Typical age of first intercourse: 16.5.[2]
* Just over half (53%) of young women report they began having sex before age 18.[3]

Contraception

* France cut condom prices to encourage young people to use them.[4]
* The proportion of under-18s who give birth has been more than halved in the last 20 years while the average age at first sex has remained stable for many years, as has the abortion rate. This has only been made possible by an increase in contraceptive use.[5]
* Emergency contraception is available over-the-counter and in schools.[5]

Abortion

* French Parliament passed a law that legalized abortion in 1979. The cost is covered by national health care.[6]
* In 2001, The French National Assembly approved a new law that extends the time in which a mother can have an abortion from 10 to 12 weeks and other changes. The law also removes parental involvement in sexual matters, including removing parental consent in abortion and access to contraceptives. It also criminalized impeding access to abortion.[7]
* France requires that each local area have at least one public hospital that offers abortion services.[8]
* RU-486 (Mifepristone) was first introduced in France in 1988. However, the manufacturer Roussel Uclaf decided to suspend marketing after death threats to staff. The French Minister of Health ordered the drug back on the market two days later calling it the "moral property of women."[9]

* More than half (56%) of the abortions performed within the approved gestational period (49 days from last menstrual period) are done using Mifepristone.[10]

Sex Education[11]

* Sex education is a "preventive" approach.
* Sex education is usually linked to Biology, Health or Natural Sciences.
* The FPA is the main agency involved in sex education provisions. The sex education model consists of prevention, teacher training programs, as well as lectures to youth, thus addressing sex education as "Life Education."
* The FPA identified the public's attitudes towards sexuality on a scale from 1 (opposed) to 9 (well accepted); France was rated as a 5.

Sexually Transmitted Infections (including HIV)

* France only started mandatory HIV case reporting in March 2003, so analysis of the HIV epidemic is difficult. The latest estimate for the cumulative HIV cases in France as of end 2003 is 96,600 (ranging between 60,700 and 176,400).[12]
* A significant decline in AIDS case incidence has been reported since 1996, primarily due to the wide-scale introduction of HAART.[12]
* Eighty-one percent of the reported AIDS cases in France are male, and 19 percent are female. Among the AIDS cases 42 percent have been infected through homo/bisexual sex, 22 percent through injecting drug use, 23 percent through heterosexual sex, and 13 percent have been infected through other or unknown sources.[12]
* Analysis of AIDS cases by transmission category suggest that the majority of early HIV cases were among IDUs. However more recently there has been a

decline in IDU related AIDS cases suggesting that HIV prevention efforts targeted at drug-injectors may have been effective.[12]

❖ An increase in gonorrhea has been observed since 1998 through a national laboratory surveillance network. The number of syphilis cases increased in 2000 in Paris among gay men, half of them were HIV positive.[12]

❖ The results of a study carried out in 2000 in gay venues in Paris show a high level of risky behavior, 30% of respondents having had casual partners had unprotected anal sex with them.[12]

❖ The French Roman Catholic bishops approved the use of condoms to help in the prevention of the HIV virus.[13]

Sexual Orientation

❖ The French Penal Code prohibits discrimination based on "moeurs" (morals, habits, or lifestyles). This includes sexual orientation. The Code of Labor law prohibits discrimination based on sexual orientation in the workplace, including civil service and armed forces positions.[14]

❖ France created a form of marital recognition for same-sex couples in 1999 (called "civil solidarity pacts," or PACS), and Germany and Portugal took similar action in 2001.[15]

❖ Both married couples and (since 1966) single people are eligible for full adoption (Code civil, Articles 343, 343-1, 345-1). The first step is to apply for an agreement of the local administration ("DDASS"). There have been cases of the application of a single man or woman being rejected on the exclusive grounds of his or her homosexuality; there have also been cases of approval being given to homosexuals who did not declare their sexual orientation; there is no known case of approval being given to open homosexuals. Unmarried couples (even heterosexual partners) cannot adopt (Code civil, Article 346).[16]

Prostitution[17]

❖ Prostitution is legal.

❖ Soliciting and procuring is illegal. A prostitute is the only one person who can use the money she earns. If she is married and purchases food for the family her husband can be prosecuted as a procurer.

Pornography[18]

❖ The legal age for viewing pornography in France is age 18.

❖ Extremely violent or graphic pornography is considered X-rated, may be shown only in specific theaters, and may not be displayed to minors. Incurs special taxes on revenue (33% for X-rated movies, 50% for pornographic online services).

Resources

▶ Association Recherche Sexologique du Sud-Ouest (ARS SO); Bordeauz Rive Droite, Route Bergerac, F-33370, Fargues-St.-Hilaine, France.

▶ Fondateur de L'Association Mondiale de Sexology; 72, Quai Louis Bleriot, 75016, Paris France.

▶ Sexologies-European Journal of Medical Sociology; 21, Place Alexandre Labadie, 13001 Marseilles.

▶ Syndicat National des Medecins Sexologues (SNMS); 77 Rue Lakana, IF-37000, Tours, France.

▶ Mouvement Francais pour le Planning Familial (MFPF), 4 Square St Irenee, 75011 Paris France. Tel: 33 (1) 48 07 29 10. Website: http://www.planning-familial.org/

GERMANY

**GERMANY
(FEDERAL REPUBLIC OF GERMANY)**
POPULATION: 82,422,299

CAPITAL: BERLIN
POPULATION: 3,933,300

Major Cities:	Berlin, Hamburg, Munich, Cologne
Ethnic Groups:	German 92%; Turkish 2%
Languages:	German (official)
Major Religions:	Protestant 34%, Roman Catholic 34%, Muslim 4%
GDP per capita (PPP):	$30,400
Urban Population:	87%
Infant Mortality:	4 per 1,000 live births
Life Expectancy:	Females: 82 years; Males: 76 years
Adult Literacy:	100%
Health Care System:	Socialized system; 1 doctor per 313 persons.

References
❏ *The World Almanac and Book of Facts* (2006). NY: World Almanac Education Group.
❏ *The World Factbook* http://www.cia.gov/cia/publications/factbook/ Accessed June 25, 2006.
❏ *World Reference Atlas* (2005). NY: Dorling Kindersley Publishing.

Sexual Activity

❖ The legal age for consent is 14.[1]

❖ Over half (58%) of young women say they began having sex before the age of 18.[2]

Contraception

❖ Oral contraceptive pills, IUDs, barrier methods and sterilization are available and covered by insurance.[3]

❖ Women under 20 years of age in Germany's eastern states can legally obtain oral contraception free.[3]

❖ Tetragynon®, a version of the Yuzpe regimen, is sold as a post-coital pregnancy prevention and is purported to reduce the chances of pregnancy by 75%.[3]

❖ Oral and emergency contraception methods are available only by prescription. However, some health facilities provide 24-hr telephone referrals to sources of emergency contraception.[4]

Abortion

❖ In 1995, in order to reconcile the abortion laws of the former East and West German republics, Germany adopted a law broadening the circumstances under which abortion is permitted in what was West Germany, while increasing the restrictions on abortion in the former East Germany. Under the new law, abortion cannot be prosecuted during the first 14 weeks of pregnancy and is available without limitation as to reason. But, women seeking abortions must meet several procedural requirements, and most abortions are no longer covered by national health insurance.[5]

❖ An abortion may only be performed after a 3 day waiting period.[6]

❖ Abortion is still considered shameful. Anti-abortion sentiment is precipitating demonstrations and picketing outside abortion clinics in Germany.[7]

❖ In 1999, RU-486 (Mifepristone) was approved for marketing in Germany.[8]

Sex Education

❖ The Pregnancy and Family Support Act of 1992 makes it the duty of the Federal and Laender governments to improve sex education.[3]

❖ Pro Familia, Germany's family planning association, provides counseling and sex education. There is some public funding for sex education, but only a fraction of what was initially planned.[9]

❖ Information and focus in AIDS education has been to provide counseling and care for HIV/AIDS patients and the prevention of discrimination towards persons with positive HIV/AIDS status. The mass media provides messages promoting safe sex, and the schools encourage AIDS education.[10]

Sexually Transmitted Infections (including HIV)

❖ The Federal Venereal Disease Control Act (FVDC) of 1953 focuses on syphilis, gonorrhea, chancroid and lymphogranulomatosis and includes strict regulations with reporting and notification requirements. While the disease is transmissible, people with STIs are prohibited from breast-feeding, having sexual intercourse, and performing professional activities, which carry the risk of transmitting the disease.[10]

❖ The 1961 Federal Epidemics Control Act (FECA) makes communicable diseases the responsibility of the Public Health Service and includes the surveillance of infected persons.[10]

❖ The opening of the wall between the East and West and the rise of unrestricted travel raises the chances that STIs will be harder to contain or trace.[10]

❖ An estimated 40,000–45,000 people were living with HIV/AIDS in Germany at the end of 2003.[11]

- HIV testing is systematic among blood donors and recommended for pregnant women, with an estimated coverage of 50-80%.[11]

- Since 1993, laboratories and, since 1998, clinicians report anonymously newly diagnosed HIV infections to a national HIV database. Clinician reports are provided for over 90% of cases and contain a name-based code to allow for detection of duplicate reports.[11]

- About half of all infections are in MSM. About 20% of infections are in immigrants from high prevalence areas. Additional 18% are heterosexually infected. The number and percentage of IDU were decreasing in the 90s, currently the numbers are stable, about 9% of all infections are in IDU.[11]

Sexual Orientation

- A minimum of 10,000 homosexual men were forced by the Nazis to wear pink triangles and be confined to concentration campus during World War II.[12]

- By 1948, some toleration of homosexuality had begun, but it took until 1968-69 for the Imperial Penal Code of 1871, Paragraph 175 and criminalization of homosexuality (1897) to be abolished.[13]

- In June 1992, the German State Brandenburg enacted a new constitution instituting State recognition of non-marriage partnerships.[13]

- In 1993, Berlin included sexual orientation as a non-discrimination criteria in its constitution.[13]

- In 2001, registered partnerships were recognized. Same-sex couples have a status comparable to marriage. However, adoption and child custody rights are withheld.[13]

- Gays cannot be excluded from military service, but homosexual relations between military personnel on duty is illegal.[13]

Prostitution

- Prostitution is legal in Germany. Communities can limit areas used and the times of day prostitutes work.[14]

- Prostitutes must be registered with the health authorities.[14]

- Pimping and promoting prostitution are illegal.[14]

- EROS Centers can be found where prostitutes rent a room and sit in the window to lure customers.[14]

- In 2003, the government changed the law in an effort to improve the legal situation of prostitutes. However, the social stigmatization of prostitutes persists, forcing most prostitutes to lead a double life. Authorities consider the common exploitation of women from Eastern Europe to be the main problem associated with the occupation.[15]

Pornography

- All forms of sexual, pornographic, and/or obscene material are easily available in Germany, the soft variety from newsstands and television, the harder types in numerous shops where even the most extreme examples are available under the counter.[16]

- Child pornography is banned. Although law defines a child to be a person up to the age of 14, no pornographic material may involve persons below the age of 18. Hard pornography (violence and animal related) may not be produced or distributed; possession is allowed. Hardcore pornography is restricted to buyers of 18 years or older. If a store is accessible to minors, the material must not be on display and may only be sold discreetly and by request. Special parental privilege needed to show hardcore pornography to their children for educational purposes. The law defines pornography to be hardcore pornography, thus anything else is not restricted.[17]

Resources

▶ Pro Familia: Bundesverband, Stresemannallee 3, 60596 Frankfurt am Main, Germany. Tel: 49 (69) 639 002. Website: *http://www.profamilia.de/topic/home*

▶ National AIDS Committee (Nationaler AIDS-Beirat - NAB), Federal Ministry for Health, 53108 Bonn, Germany. Tel: (228) 941-3200

▶ German Society for Sexual Research (Deutsche Gesellschaft fur Sexualforschung - DGSF), c/o Klinik fuer Psychotherapie und Psychosomatik, Niemannsweg 147, 24105 Kiel, Germany. Tel: (431) 597-2655

GREECE

<table>
<tr><td></td></tr>
</table>

GREECE

POPULATION: 10,688,058

CAPITAL: ATHENS

POPULATION: 3,247,000

Major Cities:	Athens, Thessoloniki
Ethnic Groups:	Greek 98%
Languages:	Greek (official) 99%, English, French
Major Religions:	Greek Orthodox 98% (official)
GDP per capita (PPP):	$22,200
Urban Population:	60%
Infant Mortality:	5 per 1,000 births
Life Expectancy:	Females: 82 years; Males: 77 years
Adult Literacy:	95%
Health Care System:	Physicians: 1 per 263 persons.

References

❏ *The World Almanac and Book of Facts* (2006). NY: World Almanac Education Group.

❏ *The World Factbook* http://www.cia.gov/cia/publications/factbook/ Accessed June 25, 2006.

❏ *World Reference Atlas* (2005). NY: Dorling Kindersley Publishing.

Sexual Activity

❖ Age of consent for heterosexual and homosexual relations is 15 years of age.[1]

❖ Teen pregnancies are rising. For example, in 1985 they accounted for 5% of all pregnancies but this had doubled by to over 10% by 1990.[2]

Contraception

❖ Until 1980, family planning was illegal in Greece; abortion was mainly used as a form of birth control, and despite being illegal, it was widespread.[3]

❖ The condom represents the main form of modern contraception (35% of all users).[4]

❖ Over 60% of women rely on withdrawal as their only contraceptive method.[5]

❖ The pill has been available without a prescription since 1963.[5]

❖ The cost of modern contraception is not expensive in comparison with the cost of abortion: The Pill: 900–1,200 drachmas (US $35–45) per month; The IUD cost 3,000 drachmas (US $115) with free insertion through the family planning centers; The condom: 80-100 drachmas (US $3–$4) per condom.[4]

❖ Emergency contraception is not yet available.[5]

Abortion

❖ Abortion is the primary method of family planning, despite the increasing availability of most modern forms of contraception.[4]

❖ Until the Second World War, abortion was strictly opposed except on medical grounds. Abortion laws were liberalized in 1978, and again in 1986, allowing a woman to have a free abortion in a public hospital up to the 12th week (later abortions are permitted on various grounds).[3]

❖ Women under 18 must have parental consent.[2]

❖ Roughly two out of three women have had an abortion with a resulting ratio of 1.3 live births to 1.8 abortions per woman.[6]

❖ Private abortions cost about US $200 and are usually performed immediately, in contrast to the state system which requires bureaucratic procedures and consequent delays.[6]

❖ RU-486 (Mifepristone) was approved for marketing in 1999, but is not yet available.[7]

Sex Education

❖ Sex education does not exist in the school curricula; in fact Greece is one of the few European countries without sex education.[8]

❖ Although family planning clinics were first established in the early 1980s, they are not currently involved in school sex education per se; they are involved in trying to influence public and political opinion and the training of health workers.[9]

Sexually Transmitted Infections (including HIV)[10]

❖ An estimated 6,521 people were living with HIV/AIDS in Greece at the end of 2003. Of these 80% are men and 20% women.

❖ Overall, sexual transmission accounts for the vast majority of reported HIV cases, with 45% of cases homo/bi-sexual and 17% heterosexual. A further 4% of cases are among injecting drug users..

❖ Among 1,214 cases infected through heterosexual contact the majority are women. The majority of heterosexual cases reported in 2002–2003 (45%) are cases from countries with generalized HIV epidemics.

* HIV testing is mandatory and systematic in blood donors and recommended for pregnant women, STI patients, IDUs and persons at high risk for HIV. Case reporting is mandatory and confidential by law for both HIV and AIDS cases at national level.

Sexual Orientation

* "Sexual orientation" as a non-discrimination category is not included in either the Constitution or the penal code.[11]
* A law introduced in 1981 on public health allows forced testing of gay men for STD's. It has been used by police to harass gays.[11]
* Homosexuality is banned among officers in military service.[12]

Prostitution[13]

* Prostitution is legal.
* Women must register and attend clinics for regular examinations, in some cases as frequently as twice weekly.

Pornography

* Both heterosexual and homosexual pornography is a thriving industry.[14]
* Bookstores and X-rated back rooms of video stores display heterosexual and homosexual materials on adjacent shelves.[14]
* Many Greek paintings (erotic art) show sexual intercourse, fellatio, orgies, pedophilic behavior and a variety of other sexual behaviors.[15]

Resources

▶ Family Planning Association of Greece, Alkaiou 10, 11528 Athens Greece. Tel: 30 210 77 74 607.

▶ Greek Society of Andrology and Sexology, Chalcocondili 50, Athens.

HUNGARY

HUNGARY

POPULATION: 9,981,334

CAPITAL: **BUDAPEST**
POPULATION: 2,597,000

Major Cities:	Budapest, Debrecen, Miskolc
Ethnic Groups:	Hungarian 92%, Roma 2%
Languages:	Hungarian (official) 94%
Major Religions:	Roman Catholic 52%, Calvinist 16%, Lutheran 3%
GDP per capita (PPP):	$16,300
Urban Population:	64%
Infant Mortality:	8 per 1,000 live births
Life Expectancy:	Females: 77 years; Males: 68 years
Adult Literacy:	99%
Health Care System:	Since 1974, 99% of the population was covered and was eligible for free health care. Limited private practice is permitted; 1 doctor per 336 persons.

References

❑ *The World Almanac and Book of Facts* (2006). NY: World Almanac Education Group.
❑ *The World Factbook* http://www.cia.gov/cia/publications/factbook/ Accessed June 25, 2006.
❑ *World Reference Atlas* (2005). NY: Dorling Kindersley Publishing.

Sexual Activity

❖ The age of consent for sexual activity for heterosexuals is 14.[1]

Contraception[2]

❖ Postinor, a form of emergency contraception, was developed in Hungary.

❖ Postinor was originally promoted as the ideal method of contraception for people with infrequent sexual contacts, and it soon became one of the most widely used forms of birth control.

❖ It is believed that most Hungarian women do not keep a supply of Postinor on hand for emergencies, but that younger women are more likely to carry it in their purses.

❖ Though there is little national data about such statistics, users of emergency contraception tend to be young, unmarried women, who switch to oral contraception when in a stable relationship, and then to IUDs when their families are completed.

Abortion

❖ A "law on the protection of fetal life" was passed in December of 1992.[3]

❖ Abortion is available up to 12 weeks, with exceptions made for the following reasons: health risk to mother or fetus, rape or other sexual crime, or due to the crisis situation of the pregnant woman.

❖ Minors must have parental consent.[3]

❖ Counseling is mandatory. Women must wait three days after counseling but must have the abortion within eight days of the counseling.[3]

❖ The "crisis situation" is defined by the woman herself, but is not discussed, as it is considered a private matter.[3]

❖ Since the new law, abortion rates have declined.[5]

❖ Public opinion holds that it is the right of each woman to decide whether to terminate a pregnancy or to give birth. It is also public opinion that the father/spouse/partner should also be given consideration about such decisions.[3]

❖ Though most Hungarians believe that life begins in the womb, this belief does not affect abortion arguments for socio-economic or health reasons.[4]

Sex Education[5]

❖ Some sex education subjects exist in school curricula, though it is linked with Biology, Health, or the Natural Sciences.

❖ There is sex education for pre-adolescents, focusing on biological facts of reproduction and puberty.

❖ There is no opportunity for formal sex education training for teachers.

❖ Family Planning Association is the main agency involved in sex education.

Sexually Transmitted Infections (including HIV)[6]

❖ An estimated 2,800 people were living with HIV/AIDS in Hungary at the end of 2003.

❖ The majority of reported HIV infections are among homo/bi-sexual men, heterosexual women, with relatively fewer cases amongst IDUs. Closer analysis of heterosexual cases reveals that in 2002-2003 32% were imported cases from countries with generalized HIV epidemics.

❖ Testing is mandatory for blood donors and STI patients.

❖ A national HIV reporting system has existed since 1985.

❖ Rates of syphilis have remained lower than 4 per 100,000 through 1994.

Sexual Orientation

❖ In May 1996, Hungary became the first Eastern European country to extend traditional common-law marriage rights to homosexual couples. Gay couples who live together and have sex have all the rights of heterosexual spouses—including to inheritance and pensions—but are not allowed to adopt children.[7]

❖ Homosexuality was decriminalized in 1961. The age of consent for homosexual practices was 20 years between 1961 and 1978. In 1978 this was changed to 18 years in Section 199 Penal Code (which refers to homosexuality as "unnatural illicit sexual practices"), whereas the age of consent for heterosexuals is 14 (Section 201 Penal Code). Section 199 Penal Code provides a penalty of up to 3 years' imprisonment for a violation.[8]

❖ The state recommends to gay men, not to become a teacher or soldier.[8]

Prostitution[9]

❖ Prostitution has been legal since 1992.

❖ Prostitutes may be found in clubs (La Dolce Vita), bars, hotels, and through the newspaper "Expressz" under the headline "Szexpartnert," where you may find agencies and massage parlors.

Pornography[1]

❖ The legal age for viewing pornography is 18.

❖ Genitals on the cover of magazines are prohibited unless obscured.

Resources

▶ Family Planning Association of Hungary: Magyar Család- és Növédelmi Tudományos Társaság, Keleti Karoly u. 5)-7, 1024 Budapest Hungary. Tel: 36 (1) 345 67 2. Website: *http://www.szexinfo.hu/*

▶ Pro Familia Hungarian Scientific Society, Buai Laszl u. 2. III. em. 1, 1024 Budapest, Hungary.

INDIA

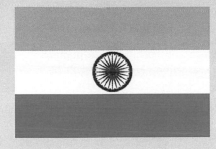

INDIA

POPULATION: 1.1 BILLION

CAPITAL: NEW DELHI

POPULATION: 15,334,000

Major Cities:	Bombay, Calcutta, Delhi, Madras
Ethnic Groups:	Indo-Aryan 72%, Dravidian 25%
Languages:	Hindi (official), English (associate official), 14 regional official languages
Major Religions:	Hindu 81%, Muslim 13%, Christian 2%
GDP per capita (PPP):	$3,300
Urban Population:	28%
Infant Mortality:	55 per 1,000 births
Life Expectancy:	Females: 66 years; Males: 64 years
Adult Literacy:	60%
Health Care System:	Government is responsible for all health care; hospitals; public/private physicians; 1 doctor per 2,157 persons.

References
❏ *The World Almanac and Book of Facts* (2006). NY: World Almanac Education Group.
❏ *The World Factbook* http://www.cia.gov/cia/publications/factbook/ Accessed June 25, 2006.
❏ *World Reference Atlas* (2005). NY: Dorling Kindersley Publishing.

Sexual Activity

❖ The legal age of consent is 16 for hetero-sexuals; homosexual sex is illegal.[1]

❖ All types of sexual interaction before marriage are forbidden; total self-restraint is advocated. Even the discussion of sex is taboo but this is slowly weakening. A study revealed that almost 16% of rural boys and 9% of college males had a sexual experience. More than 80% of the boys had their first sexual contact with a prostitute and 80% had never used a condom. 16% reported that their first sexual contact had been with a girl friend of almost the same age group.[2]

❖ The mean age at first coitus: 18 years.[2]

Contraception

❖ Nearly 50 years ago, India became the first country in the developing world to initiate a state-sponsored family planning program with the goal of lowering fertility and slowing the population growth rate.[3]

❖ The government of India has been a powerful proponent of population control. India's population policy has been characterized by a drive to reduce fertility rates and to achieve demographic goals. For example, the central government established specific demographic targets to decrease the present level of approximately 33 births per 1,000 to the low 20's by the year 2000. Moreover, targets for the numbers of users of specific types of contraception, particularly sterilization and IUDs, are also set.[4]

❖ Cash incentive programs for the recipients of sterilization and IUD services, the medical providers of such services, and the health workers who "motivate" an individual or couple to become sterilized also exist.[4]

❖ Since the mid-1970s, the Indian government has promoted sterilization, which many reject because it is irreversible and seen as a human rights violation.[3]

❖ In 1989, 43% of Indians used contraception. 72% of all contraceptive users relied heavily on sterilization. In 1993, 43% of all sterilizations were performed on women. 11.8% used condoms. 4.2% used IUD's. 3.1% used pills.[4]

❖ A group of Indian scientists is studying a contraceptive injection for men that they believe will become more popular than the vasectomy because it will be easily reversible.[5]

❖ Emergency contraception is available over-the-counter.[6]

Abortion

❖ India is an example of a country where a liberal abortion law does not ensure that women can access safe and legal procedures. India's Medical Termination of Pregnancy Act permits abortion on socio-economic grounds, and even recognizes that the anguish of an unwanted pregnancy resulting from contraceptive failure could constitute a "grave injury to the mental health of the pregnant woman" that could justify an abortion. However, only 1,800 of the 20,000 primary health centers have legally certified abortion facilities. Women with unwanted pregnancies are forced to rely on low-cost procedures, which are often undertaken by untrained practitioners under unsanitary conditions.[7]

❖ More than 20,000 women die because of unsafe abortion practices in India every year despite the fact that abortion is legal in the country, reports IPAS, a non-profit group working worldwide to reduce abortion related mortality. At five million, India has the world's largest number of unsafe abortions a year, or a quarter of the global total.[8]

❖ Unless a medical emergency exists, a legal abortion must be performed during the first 20 weeks of gestation by a registered physician in a government hospital.[9]

- A legal abortion is free of charge only if it is performed in a government hospital. These hospitals are often inaccessible, therefore the number of illegal and/or unregistered abortions are estimated to around 6 million annually.[9]
- It is estimated that unsafe abortions account for 20% of maternal deaths in India.[9]
- Female feticide is common although there are no adequate statistics available on the subject.[6]
- In an effort to halt widespread abortions of female fetuses, the Indian Parliament passed a law prohibiting doctors from telling expectant parents of their off-spring's gender. The bill also bans the advertisement and performance of ultra-sounds solely to determine gender.[10]
- Mifepristone/RU 486 (non-surgical "abortion pill"): is registered for use in India.[11]

Sex Education

- There has been no sex education at any level in the past.[2]
- Sex education has not been taught in schools because society believes it would "spoil the minds" of the children.[2]
- The Ministry of Health and Family Welfare began coordinating primary and adult education programs and is promot-ing its family planning agenda in rural areas.[10]

Sexually Transmitted Infections (including HIV)

- An estimated 5.7 million people were living with HIV/AIDS in India at the end of 2005—more than any other country in the world except South Africa.[12]
- The first case of AIDS in India was detected in 1986. Since then, HIV infec-tions have been reported in all States and Union Territories.[12]

- With a population of one billion—about half in the 15–49 year-old population—HIV epidemics in India will have a major impact on the overall spread of HIV in Asia and the Pacific, as well as globally.[12]
- The spread of HIV within India is as diverse as the societal patterns between its different regions, states and metro-politan areas. The epidemics are focused very sharply in a few southern States, with most of India having extremely low rates of infection.[12]
- An overwhelming majority of the total reported national AIDS cases—96%—were reported by only 10 of the 31 states. The major impact is being felt in Maharashtra in the west, Tamil Nadu in the south with adjacent Pondicherry, and Manipur in the northeast.[12]
- With a high prevalence of tuberculosis infection in India, the problem of tuber-culosis related to HIV infection also poses a major public health challenge.[12]
- Most HIV infections in India (more than 80% of reported AIDS cases) are due to unprotected heterosexual inter-course. Injecting drug use is the main driver of the HIV epidemics in the north-east, and there is a substantial overlap between injecting drug use and paid sex in some parts of the country. In Tamil Nadu, HIV prevalence of 50% has been found among some sex work-ers. In 2005, well below 10% of people needing antiretroviral treatment were receiving it in India (which has more than 70% of the region's total treat-ment needs).[13]
- India has no laws barring prostitutes from continuing their trades even after they discover that they are HIV-positive.[14]

Sexual Orientation[15]

- Section 377 of the Indian Penal Code criminalizes male to male sex with up to 10 years imprisonment. One of the consequences of this is to make it very difficult for males who have sex with males to access sexual health services because their behavior is against the law and through this accessing makes them visible. It further makes the availability of sexual health services for prisoners difficult.

❖ The second issue, and related to the first, is the high level of reported harassment and violence directed towards males who have sex with males both by police and members of the general public. Very often there will be a demand for sex and/or money. Reporting of these incidents is obviated by Section 377, and further compounded by the unsympathetic and sometimes violent attitudes of the police.

Prostitution

❖ Prostitution is technically illegal but widely tolerated.[14]

❖ According to health authorities, Bombay has over 100,000 prostitutes.[14]

❖ 20% of the prostitutes in Bombay are under 18, about half are infected with HIV.[16]

❖ In southwestern India, thousands of people have been dedicating their daughters to a religiously sanctioned life of prostitution for well over a millennium.[17] These girls, as young as 6, are initiated into a life of sexual slavery as servants of the gods.[18]

❖ Children's advocacy groups estimate that 300,000–400,000 children in India are involved in the sex industry.[19]

Pornography[20]

❖ No information was found Pornography is illegal and attracts several penal provisions. However, enforcement is extremely lax and pornographic materials are easily available. The law also states that only the distribution of pornography is illegal, while its creation and accessing it is not. Therefore, it is legal to access a pornographic site hosted on non-Indian servers.

Resources

▶ Family Planning Association of India (FPAI), Bajaj Bhavan, 1st Floor, Nariman Point, Mumbai 400021 India. Tel: + 91 22 202 9080.

▶ Indian Association of Sex Educators, Counselors, and Therapists (IASECT), 203 Sukhsagar, N. S. Patkar Marg., Bombay 400 007. Tel: 91-22/361-2027.

IRAN

IRAN

POPULATION: 68,688,433

CAPITAL: TEHRAN
POPULATION: 7,796,257

Major Cities:	Tehran, Estahan, Mashhad
Ethnic Groups:	Persian 51%, Azeri 24%, Gilski and Mazandarani 8%, Kurd 7%
Languages:	Persian 58%, Turkic 26%, Kurdish 9%, Luri 2%
Major Religions:	Shi'a Muslim 89%; Sunni Muslim 9%
GDP per capita (PPP):	$8,300
Urban Population:	61%
Infant Mortality:	40 per 1,000 births
Life Expectancy:	Females: 72 years; Males: 69 years
Adult Literacy:	79%
Health Care System:	Physicians: 1 per 2,538 persons.

References
❑ *The World Almanac and Book of Facts* (2006). NY: World Almanac Education Group.
❑ *The World Factbook* http://www.cia.gov/cia/publications/factbook/ Accessed June 25, 2006.
❑ *World Reference Atlas* (2005). NY: Dorling Kindersley Publishing.

Sexual Activity

❖ There is no age of consent to sexual activity outside of marriage.[1]

❖ Polygyny is regulated by Islamic custom, which permits a man to have as many as four wives simultaneously, provided that he treats them equally.[2]

❖ On May 16th 1993 the Iranian Parliament ratified a bill aimed at encouraging couples to have no more than three children. Legislation will grant special government benefits to the first three children only. This rule took affect in 1994.[3]

❖ According to Amnesty International—a 16-year-old girl was publicly hanged in Iran in August 2004 for alleged "acts incompatible with chastity" and in another case, a teenage girl with a mental age of eight is facing the death penalty for commercial sex work in Iran. Amnesty International refers to reports that say she was repeatedly raped, bore her first child aged nine and was passed from pimp to pimp before having another three children. Women around the world are regularly murdered, assaulted, beaten, stoned, mutilated and have acid thrown at them—all in the name of "honor". Honor crimes are premeditated attacks carried out by family members as punishment for deeds they believe have dishonored the family name. The victims of these crimes are overwhelmingly female.[4]

Contraception

❖ The goal of the Social and Cultural Development Plan is to reduce the total fertility rate to four children per woman by the year 2011.[5]

❖ The Government has proposed to raise levels of contraception use to 24% of women of childbearing age and to prevent 1 million unwanted births.[5]

❖ The Health Ministry distributes condoms, IUDs and birth control pills for free. Vasectomies are also free.[6]

Abortion[5]

❖ In 1973, induced abortion was legalized in Iran.

❖ After the revolution in 1979, abortion was once again made illegal on most grounds. Abortion is currently prohibited on all grounds except to save the life of a pregnant woman.

Sex Education[6]

❖ In order to get a marriage license, couples must take a segregated course in family planning.

Sexually Transmitted Infections (including HIV)[7]

❖ An estimated 31,000 people were living with HIV/AIDS in Iran at the end of 2003.

❖ The HIV epidemic in the Islamic Republic of Iran appears to be accelerating at an alarming trend. According to reports by the National AIDS program, the number of newly diagnosed HIV infections and AIDS cases in 2001 shows a three-fold increase in comparison to both years 2000 and 1999.

❖ Injecting drug use drives the epidemic in Iran. In 2001, 64% of all AIDS cases were injecting drug users.

❖ There has been a significant increase of total numbers of reported STI cases in the country during the period of 1995 to 1998. Candidiasis, Trichomoniasis, Chlamydia and Gonorrhea are the four main causes, accounting for over 60% of the cases.

Sexual Orientation

❖ Homosexuality is illegal in Iran.[8]

❖ There are eight countries with the death penalty for homosexuality: Iran is one of them (along with Afghanistan, Mauritania, Pakistan, Saudi Arabia, Sudan, United Arab Emirates and Yemen).[8]

* Sodomy is a crime, for which both partners are punished. The punishment is death if the participants are adults, of sound mind and consenting. A non-adult who engages in consensual sodomy is subject to a punishment of 74 lashes.[9]

* The punishment for lesbianism involving persons who are mature, of sound mind, and consenting, is 100 lashes. If the act is repeated three times and punishment is enforced each time, the death sentence will apply on the fourth occasion.[9]

* According to Amnesty International at least three gay men and two lesbians were killed in January 1990, as a result of the Iranian government's policy of calling for the execution of homosexuals. They were publicly beheaded.[9]

Prostitution[10]

* Prostitution is illegal in Iran.

* On May 6, 1994 an American woman, Mary Jones of Texas was arrested and convicted for prostitution in Iran. She received 80 lashes as her punishment.

Pornography[11]

* Pornography is illegal in Iran

* The Iranian Parliament has approved legislation providing for capital punishment for producers & distributors of pornographic videotapes.

* The bill that provides a maximum five years prison term and $100,000 in fines for first offenders, said the principal promoters of pornographic videos can receive the death penalty.

Resources

▶ FPA Iran, No. 2/1, 8 Street Behrooz Street, Mohseni Square Mirdamad Avenue, PO Box 19395-3518, Tehran 19119, Islamic Republic of Iran. Tel: 9821 222 3944.

▶ Islamic Women's Institute (13643), No. 1-275 Hedayat St., N. Saddi, Tehran, Islamic Republic of Iran. Tel: 98 21 3115656.

IRELAND

IRELAND

POPULATION: 4,062,235

CAPITAL: **DUBLIN**

POPULATION: 1,018,500

Major Cities:	Dublin, Cork
Ethnic Groups:	Celtic, English
Languages:	English predominates, Irish (Gaelic) spoken by minority (both official)
Major Religions:	Roman Catholic 88%; Church of Ireland 3%
GDP per capita (PPP):	$41,000
Urban Population:	59%
Infant Mortality:	5 per 1,000 births
Life Expectancy:	Females: 81 years; Males: 75 years
Adult Literacy:	100%
Health Care System:	Physicians: 1 per 588 persons.

References

❏ *The World Almanac and Book of Facts* (2006). NY: World Almanac Education Group.
❏ *The World Factbook* http://www.cia.gov/cia/publications/factbook/ Accessed June 25, 2006.
❏ *World Reference Atlas* (2005). NY: Dorling Kindersley Publishing.

Sexual Activity[1]

❖ The age of consent is 17.

Contraception

❖ Contraception was restricted in the Irish Republic by the Censorship of Publications Act, 1929, and the Criminal Law Amendment Act, 1935 (reformed in 1979). Limited to medical prescription through pharmacies by the Health (Family Planning) Act of 1979, condoms were de-restricted (including vending machines) in June 1993.[2]

❖ State funding services is restricted to centers providing advice on natural family planning methods. Contraceptives are available form some pharmacies, the condom being the most popular.[3]

❖ Even though Ireland is a highly religious country, with much more conservative values regarding love, sex, and marriage, Roman Catholic adolescents have a relatively positive attitude toward the use of contraception.[4]

❖ Emergency contraception is not available in Ireland.[5]

Abortion

❖ Legislation: At the root of legislation is the 1861 (British) Offenses Against the Person Act, which makes providing "unlawful" abortions illegal. Due to the wording, this law is poorly defined and was used to back up earlier decisions to perform abortions in order to save the life of the woman.[6]

❖ In addition to this law, British parliament passed the Infant Life (Preservation) Act, which makes it unlawful to perform an abortion when the infant is capable of being born alive (28 weeks or more in gestational age), unless it is performed to save the life of the mother. This act was eventually enacted as the Criminal Justice (Northern Ireland) Act in 1945.[6]

❖ Since clarity was still lacking on these laws, in 1967 the Abortion Act was enacted in Britain which stated that abortions may be carried out, as deemed by two doctors, if the life of the mother, mentally or physically, is in danger, or of the infant will suffer serious mental or physical abnormalities or handicap after birth.[6]

❖ In the 1980s, the Right to Life movement was gaining power in Ireland, and they pushed until, in 1983, the Eighth Amendment to the Constitution of the Republic of Ireland was inaugurated, which absolutely made abortion illegal, unless the life of the mother is in danger.[6]

❖ In the interpretation of the law, the "respect" and "the right to life of the unborn," the anti choice advocates in SPUC (Society for the Protection of the Unborn Child) in 1986 were able to prevent two counseling agencies for women from giving counseling about abortion. After appealing to the European Commission, these counseling agencies were allowed to open in 1991. However, a legal battle initiated by SPUC made the publication of any information about British abortion clinics was declared illegal and unconstitutional.[6]

❖ This was changed during the November 1992 referendum, and the provision of such information is now permitted. In February 1992, a 14 year-old rape victim was prevented by the High Court to go to Britain to obtain an abortion. This led to a Supreme Court ruling allowing her to obtain an abortion, since her life was in danger due to suicide. Thus, in November, the freedom to travel abroad and obtain information was approved.[7]

❖ Currently abortion is illegal in all circumstances other than when necessary to preserve the pregnant woman's life. In the summer of 2001 Irish pro-choice activists welcomed a visit by the Women on Waves ship, a fully equipped reproductive health care clinic that travels to countries where abortion is illegal. The visit attracted national and international attention to the lack of safe, legal abortion in Ireland. The trip to Ireland was the ship's "maiden visit" and was supported by a group of over 200 Irish volunteers nationwide. Over 6,000 Irish women go to Britain for abortions each year, yet cannot avail themselves of the same service in their home country. Even those women who face life-threatening pregnancies must suffer through many obstacles to obtain abortion services in Ireland. The "Irish solution to the Irish problem"—exporting the abortion issue to Britain—is no solution for women facing a crisis pregnancy. The Women on Waves visit was an enormous success in Ireland. Although complications with the Dutch licensing laws led to a decision not to provide abortions at sea during this visit, volunteers successfully provided abortion information and contraceptive access, including emergency contraceptives, that would otherwise have been unavailable in Ireland. The ship served over 300 women while also drawing international attention to the enormous difficulties created by Ireland's draconian abortion laws.[8]

Sex Education

❖ In Ireland, sex education does not exist in school curricula.[9]

❖ The Irish Family Planning Association (IFPA) has a project focused on young people entitled, Social Education, Contraception, and Sexuality in Ireland, which provides materials, a telephone hotline, and posters. The aim is to encourage young people's right to enjoy their sexual lives with dignity, respect, and equality; to make free and informed choices, and to make accessible the information and services necessary for young people to enjoy safe and happy sexual lives.[3]

Sexually Transmitted Infections (including HIV)[10]

❖ Since the start of the epidemic and as of June 2003, 3,216 persons had been diagnosed with HIV. The majority (34%) are drug injectors. A further 32% are heterosexual and 22% homo/bi-sexual cases.

❖ The epidemiology of HIV infection in Ireland has changed considerably in the last ten years.

❖ In recent years the incidence of both new injecting drug use and homo/bi-sexual cases has declined and remained relatively stable, however there have been marked increases in heterosexual cases.

Sexual Orientation

❖ In June 1993, despite strong opposition of the Roman Catholic Church, homosexual act between consenting males was made legal. The age of consent was set at 17, the same age for heterosexuals. The consent laws already cover lesbians.[11]

❖ In 1989 the Prohibition of Incitement to Hatred Act was enacted, making it illegal to incite hatred against lesbians and gay men.[11]

❖ The Equal Status Bill, which would have outlawed discrimination in non-employment areas, was passed by the Irish Parliament in 1997 with the support of all political parties. However it was not passed into law because the Supreme Court found some sections to be unconstitutional.[12]

❖ The Unfair Dismissals (Amendment) Act 1993 provides that dismissal on the grounds of an employee's sexual orientation will automatically be deemed unfair.[12]

❖ The law on adoption discriminates against lesbians and gay men as well as all unmarried persons. You can only adopt a child if you are legally married, widowed or judicially separated people.[12]

Prostitution[13]

❖ Prostitution is illegal.

Pornography[13]

❖ Pornography is illegal.

Resource

▶ Irish Family Planning Association (IFPA), 60 Amiens Street, Dublin 1, Ireland.

Tel: 353 (1) 806 94 44. Website: *http://www.ifpa.ie/*

ISRAEL

ISRAEL

POPULATION: 6,352,117

CAPITAL: JERUSALEM

POPULATION: 695,000

Major Cities:	Jerusalem, Tel Aviv-Yafo, Haifa
Ethnic Groups:	Jewish 80%, Non-Jewish (mostly Arab) 20%
Languages:	Hebrew (official) and Arabic (used officially for Arab minority), English
Religions:	Judaism 80%, Muslim 15%, Arab Christian 2%
GDP per capita (PPP):	$24,600
Urban Population:	91%
Infant Mortality:	7 per 1,000 births
Life Expectancy:	Females: 82 years; Males: 77 years
Literacy:	95%
Health Care System:	Publicly funded health centers/clinics; 1 doctor per 350 people.

References

❏ *The World Almanac and Book of Facts* (2006). NY: World Almanac Education Group.
❏ *The World Factbook* http://www.cia.gov/cia/publications/factbook/ Accessed June 25, 2006.
❏ *World Reference Atlas* (2005). NY: Dorling Kindersley Publishing.

Sexual Activity[1]

❖ The legal age of consent is 16.

Contraception[2]

❖ Modern contraception is widely available. Two studies among Israeli Jews found that they relied heavily on the IUD as a form of contraceptive. Sterilization was little used and withdrawal, although in decline, was still relied on to a significant extent.[2]

❖ The "morning after" pill, Postinor 2, became available over–the-counter in 2002.[3]

Abortion

❖ Abortion has been allowed since 1952.[4]

❖ An abortion must be performed by a physician in a recognized medical institution, with the written consent of the pregnant woman. A legal abortion requires the approval of a committee made up of two physicians and a social worker. The committee members must be appointed by the Director of the hospital where the abortion will be performed, or by the Minister of Health or a person appointed by him if the procedure is to be performed in another recognized medical institution.[4]

❖ Abortions performed for medical reasons are paid for by the government, as well as for any reason if the woman is under 18; the woman pays for abortions performed on other grounds.[5]

❖ RU-486 (Mifepristone) was approved for marketing in 1999.[6]

Sex Education

❖ Sex education is relatively new in Israel. Within the past 20 years, it has grown from a sporadic, peripheral activity to a recognized and acceptable subject.[7]

❖ The Israel family Planning Association is run from the center of Tel Aviv. It provides training on sex education and family planning. The Association hosts an information resource center with books, journals, videos and they also produce their own educational materials in Hebrew and Russian. They also run special educational projects on HIV/AIDS and safer sex.[2]

Sexually Transmitted Infections (including HIV)[8]

❖ An estimated 3,802 people were living with HIV/AIDS in Israel at the end of 2003.

❖ Since the mid-90's there has been a slight but steady increase in new HIV cases detected annually in Israel. More cases are found amongst IDUs, especially among new immigrants and also a mild increase among young people (ages 21–29) is detected, most of whom originating from countries with a generalized epidemic.

❖ An HIV/AIDS registry has existed since the beginning of the epidemic. HIV testing is systematic among blood donors and prisoners and among select groups of immigrants from HIV-hyper-endemic countries. Testing is confidential and free of charge for any person requesting the service.

❖ Testing is done at all community clinics, all across the country.

❖ Health education programs are developed for both the general population and for groups with risk behaviors. Treatment and follow-up are specialized in regionally distributed AIDS centers, which can provide adequate follow-up and HAART treatment to all adherent patients.

Sexual Orientation

❖ Israel's Knesset has passed a law prohibiting employers from discriminating against employees and job applicants because of sexual orientation.[9]

❖ Until 1988 male homosexuality was punishable under Section 351 of the Penal Code, with up to ten years' imprisonment, although there was already a policy of non-prosecution. In that year Section 351 was repealed by the Knesset.[10]

❖ The army permits homosexuals to serve, but a 1993 directive cautions that they may be a security risk and should be checked on case by case; homosexuals are barred from top-secret jobs in army intelligence.[11]

Prostitution[12]

❖ Prostitution is legal in Israel. What is illegal is a second party making money off of this practice. Hence, pimping is illegal.

❖ Renting an apartment to a working girl is illegal because the rent is money made from prostitution.

❖ Massage and Escort services are illegal but usually not prosecuted.

Pornography

❖ Pornography in Israel is legal. Women are portrayed in magazines and on the street as objects. Cruelty in terms of degrading women sexually is seen as second nature to this country.[13]

❖ The legal age for viewing pornography in Israel is 18 years.[1]

Resources

▶ Institute for Sex Therapy. Sheba Medical Center, Tel Hashomer.

▶ Israel Family Planning Association. 9, Rambam Street, Tel-Aviv, 65601.

▶ Ministry of Education & Culture. Psychological and Counseling Services, 2 Devorah Hanevia Street, Jerusalem.

ITALY

ITALY

POPULATION: 58,133,509

CAPITAL: ROME (ROMA)

POPULATION: 3,550,900

Major Cities:	Milan, Naples, Rome, Turin
Ethnic Groups:	Italian, small ethnic minorities of German, French, Slovene, Albanian
Languages:	Italian (official), German, French, Slovene
Major Religions:	Roman Catholic 90%
Annual Income per Person	$29,200
Urban Population:	67%
Infant Mortality:	6 per 1,000 births
Life Expectancy:	Females: 83 years; Males: 77 years
Adult Literacy:	99%
Health Care System:	National health plan, private hospitals; 1 doctor per 909 persons.

References

❏ *The World Almanac and Book of Facts* (2006). NY: World Almanac Education Group.
❏ *The World Factbook* http://www.cia.gov/cia/publications/factbook/ Accessed June 25, 2006.
❏ *World Reference Atlas* (2005). NY: Dorling Kindersley Publishing.

Sexual Activity

❖ The age of consent for heterosexual and homosexual sex in Italy is 14.[1]

❖ 25% of high school students are sexually active, though uninformed about birth control and disease prevention. [2]

Contraception

❖ Contraceptive use was legalized in 1971. Prior to that time, contraceptives were allowed only for medical reasons, though transgressions were tolerated.[3]

❖ Despite the low rates of contraceptive use, Italy has one of the lowest fertility rates in the world.[3]

❖ There is widespread ignorance in reproductive matters.[4]

❖ There has been a concern among legislators that induced abortion would become a method of family planning. Nevertheless, it has been mainly used as an emergency measure after the failure of contraceptives.[4]

Abortion

❖ Abortion is allowed for social, socio-economic, or socio-medical reasons up to 90 days.[5]

❖ It is allowed for medical or eugenic reasons, or because of rape or other sexual crimes only, after 90 days.[5]

❖ Women must have a doctor's certificate and wait at least one week.[5]

❖ Minors need parental permission.[5]

❖ Counseling is mandatory.[5]

❖ Illegal abortions are numerous.[5]

❖ Abortions are free of charge.[6]

❖ Medical personnel who are opposed to abortion can, in advance, declare their conscientious objection, and may be excused from performing abortions.[6]

❖ The abortion rate has declined by 39% since the 1980s.[7]

Sex Education

❖ Sex education is not provided in schools, and there are few family planning programs.[6]

❖ There is an interest in schools to implement sex education programs.[8]

❖ The government removed all references to condoms in its campaign against AIDS.[9]

❖ Italy's Family Planning Association (UICEMP) focuses on information, education, and training courses for health service personnel and social workers in the state family planning clinics, for teachers, and for others working with young people.[10]

Sexually Transmitted Infections (including HIV)

❖ HIV reporting exists only in six regions/provinces out of 20 regions, so analysis of the HIV epidemic is difficult. The most recent estimate for the cumulative number of people living with HIV/AIDS in Italy as of the end of 2003 is 120,000 (ranging between 110,000 and 130,000).[11]

❖ Early on in the epidemic the main route of transmission was through injecting drug users, however in recent years new infections are predominantly transmitted sexually. Around 40 percent of new HIV infections are attributed to heterosexual sex, 35 percent to IDUs and 20 percent to homo/bisexual sex.[11]

❖ The rise in the incidence of heterosexual cases is mainly caused by an increase of imported cases from countries with generalized epidemics. In 1994 just under 2 percent of AIDS cases were found among foreigners whereas in 2003 around 20 percent of AIDS cases are among non-Italians.[11]

❖ Police cannot keep criminals with AIDS in custody, as a 1992 decree stipulates that Italian prisoners with AIDS must be released from prison, but should remain under house arrest. Thousands of prisoners have been released under this law.[9]

❖ Genital warts are the most frequently diagnosed STI with 30% of STI clinic patients infected.[12]

❖ Italy has a universal Hepatitis B vaccine program. There are approximately 9,000 deaths each year due to Hepatitis B, but this figure is slowly declining.[13]

Sexual Orientation

❖ The penal code contains no anti-lesbian or anti-gay provisions. The age of consent for heterosexual and homosexual acts is 14.[14]

❖ In the workplace, all gay men and lesbians who have been fired on grounds of sexual orientation have won their cases, because private non-criminal acts cannot be considered grounds for dismissal.[14]

❖ Since 1996, homosexuals have equal legal and financial rights in long-term relationships.[14]

❖ In Italy, only married couples can adopt, so gay and lesbian couples or single people are automatically excluded. The institution of custody can be granted to single people if a judge so rules. In some cases homosexuality has not been judged an obstacle to being granted custody.[14]

❖ In Italy, homosexuals were excluded in the military until 1985, when the ban was lifted. Today, if a man admits that he is a homosexual, he is not required to serve in the military, though he may choose to do so.[15]

Prostitution[16]

❖ Prostitution is legal.

❖ Streetwalking is legal, but operating/working in a brothel are not.

❖ In the past ten years girls from Eastern Europe and West Africa have swelled street-walkers' numbers to an estimated 50,000. Around Milan, some 5,000 girls cater to about 60,000 customers a night.

Pornography[1]

❖ Legal age for viewing pornography is 18 years.

Resources

▶ Associazione per la Ricerca in Sessuologia (ARS), Via Angelo Cappi 1/8. II 16126 Genova.

▶ Centro Italiano di Sessuologia, Via della Lungarina, 65, Rome, 00153.

▶ Instituto di Sessuologia di Savona, 17026 Noli, Via la Malta, 5, Savona.

▶ Unione Italiana Educazione Matrimoniale e Prematrimoniale (UICEMP), Via Eugenio Chiesa 1, 20122 Milan Italy. Tel: 39 (02) 545 66 87. Website: *http://www.uicemp.org/*

JAPAN

JAPAN

POPULATION: 127,463,611

CAPITAL: **TOKYO**

POPULATION: 35,327,000

Major Cities:	Tokyo, Osaka, Nagoya, Sapporo, Kyoto
Ethnic Groups:	Japanese 99%
Languages:	Japanese (official)
Major Religions:	Buddhism and Shintoism shared by 84%
GDP per capita (PPP):	$31,500
Urban Population:	79%
Infant Mortality	3 per 1,000 births
Life Expectancy:	Females: 85 years; Males: 78 years
Literacy:	99%
Health Care System:	The combination of public & private funding has created an insurance pension system for hospitals, clinics, physicians; 1 doctor per 588 persons.

References

❏ *The World Almanac and Book of Facts* (2006). NY: World Almanac Education Group.
❏ *The World Factbook http://www.cia.gov/cia/publications/factbook/* Accessed June 25, 2006.
❏ *World Reference Atlas* (2005). NY: Dorling Kindersley Publishing.

Sexual Activity

❖ Legal age of consent is 16.[1]

❖ Official figures show that Japanese schoolchildren are having more sex than ever before, and that many are shunning condoms, unaware of the risks of contracting HIV and other sexually transmitted infections (STIs). A 2005 survey found nearly 40 per cent of senior high school students aged 15 to 18 have had sex. Nearly half of 17-year-old girls have had sex, compared with 17 per cent in 1990.[2]

Contraception

❖ Birth control pills were not legalized in Japan until 1996.[3]

❖ The choice of modern contraceptive methods is very limited. Low-dose pills, IUDs, injectables, and implants have not been approved for use and the diaphragm is no longer produced in Japan due to lack of demand.[4]

❖ High dose oral contraceptives are prescribed to between 500,000 and 800,000 women for supposedly therapeutic purposes such as menstrual disorders, but in reality they are used for contraception. As a consequence, Japanese women tend to have a negative view of the Pill.[4]

❖ As contraceptive choices are so limited in Japan, more than 80% of couples use the condom.[4]

Abortion

❖ Legal restrictions were lifted in 1948, legalizing abortion in the first 5 months of pregnancy. All legal abortions must be performed within medical facilities at the compliance of a physician assigned by a local medical association. When the pregnancy is a result of rape or incest, the abortion can be performed without the legal consent of the woman.[5]

❖ Married women seeking an abortion must have the consent of her spouse.[5]

❖ Japan has an average of 300,000 to 400,000 abortions per year.[5]

❖ The abortion rate has declined by 47% since 1975.[7]

Sex Education

❖ Sex education in schools is poor, and teenagers are often left without sufficient family planning information and services.[1]

❖ Guidelines for HIV/AIDS education in schools set by the Ministry of Education:[8]

♦ As a part of hygiene education, all grade schools must teach students that HIV is a blood-borne infection.

♦ Middle schools will teach students about HIV/AIDS in the context of other sexually transmitted diseases.

♦ High schools are permitted to mention condoms as protection against HIV infection.

❖ The Ministry of Education believes that teachers should teach HIV/AIDS prevention to students without mentioning sexual intercourse.[8]

Sexually Transmitted Infections (including HIV)

❖ An estimated 12,000 people were living with HIV/AIDS in Japan at the end of 2003.

❖ HIV prevalence rates in Japan continue to remain well below 1% for most HIV-risk behavior groups, except among female sex workers of foreign nationality (2.7% from 1987–1999).[9]

❖ Most reported HIV/AIDS cases in Japan during the mid-to-late 1980s and early 1990s were due to HIV infected blood products that were imported for the treatment of hemophilia patients; a third of the AIDS cases (33.3%) reported in 1988 were in hemophilia patients infected through imported blood coagulation factor products. The high percentage of hemophilia AIDS cases is still the distinctive characteristic of HIV infection in Japan and is not seen in other countries in the world. [9]

❖ However in 2000, about 78% of newly diagnosed HIV infections appear to have been acquired through sexual contact.[9]

❖ One of the characteristics in recent years is that the infection through sexual contacts in Japan is getting higher among Japanese men.[9]

❖ Almost all HIV infections in Japan are related to imported infections (including hemophilia infections) and then some limited transmission from these infected persons to their regular sex partners.[9]

❖ Behavioral data show low condom use, both in the general population and among female sex workers (6% to 25%).[9]

❖ Higher rates of Chlamydia among females, and well as a doubling of induced abortions among teenage women, indicate increased rates of unprotected sexual intercourse among young people.[10]

Sexual Orientation[11]

❖ There are no legal proscriptions of homosexuality in Japan, nor any laws concerning the practice of sodomy - the absence of legal codes forbidding homosexuality is somewhat illusory, because societal rather than statutory regulations are preeminent.

❖ Homosexual behaviors are neither forbidden not heavily stigmatized in modern Japan, provided they respect the prevailing framework of social and familial responsibilities. However, there remains no place in Japanese society for the exclusively gay or lesbian individual who is unwilling or unable to sublimate his or her sexual identity and pursue marriage.

❖ In 1995, following international pressure from gay groups, the Japanese Society of Psychiatry and Neurology removed homosexuality from its list of disorders. The society will now rely on the World Health Organization's disease-classification manual, which considers gayness okay.

Prostitution[12]

❖ Vaginal prostitution is against the law and fellatio prostitution is legal, as women who perform fellatio for money are not considered prostitutes in Japan.

Pornography

❖ Child pornography is illegal.[1]

❖ The Japanese government has proposed to set up an independent search to control the transmission of obscene or criminal material over the Internet.[13]

❖ Sexually explicit comics for women are quite popular and they often seem to feature rape themes or other depictions of forced sexual submission.[14]

❖ Nearly 80% of commercial child pornography on the internet originates in Japan.[15]

Resources

▶ Family Planning Federation of Japan, Hoken Kaikan Shinkan Bldg, 1-10 Ichigaya Tamachi, Shinjuku, Tokyo 162-0843.

▶ Japanese Association for Sex Education. (JASE). Miyata Bldg. 1-3 Kanada Jinbocho, Chiyoda-Ku, Tokyo 101.

▶ Japanese Association of Sex Educators, Counselors and Therapists (JASECT), JASE Clinic, 3F Shin-Anoyama Bldg. (West), 1-1 Minami, Aoyama, 1-chome Minato-Ku, Tokyo 107.

▶ Japan Institute for Research in Education. 4-3-6-702 Kozimachi Chiyodaku, Tokyo 7102.

KENYA

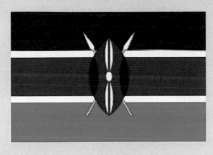

KENYA
POPULATION: 34,707,817

CAPITAL: NAIROBI
POPULATION: 3,064,800

Major Cities:	Nairobi, Mombasa
Ethnic Groups:	Kikuyu 22%, Luhya 14%, Luo 13%, Kalenjin 12%, Kamba 11%
Languages:	Kiswahili, English (both official), numerous indigenous languages
Major Religions:	Protestant 45%, Roman Catholic 33%, indigenous beliefs 10%, Muslim 10%
GDP per capita (PPP):	$1,100
Urban Population:	32%
Infant Mortality:	59 per 1,000 live births
Life Expectancy:	Females: 48 years; Males: 50 years
Adult Literacy:	85%
Health Care System:	1 doctor per 10,150 people.

References
- ❑ *The World Almanac and Book of Facts* (2006). NY: World Almanac Education Group.
- ❑ *The World Factbook* http://www.cia.gov/cia/publications/factbook/ Accessed June 25, 2006.
- ❑ *World Reference Atlas* (2005). NY: Dorling Kindersley Publishing.

Sexual Activity

* Legal age of consent is 16 for heterosexuals; it is illegal for homosexuals.[1]
* Most women have their first child before age 18.[2]
* First sexual contact can be as early as 10–12 in both boys and girls; sexuality has a lot to do with culture, education, family units and economic factors.[2]
* Young girls who become pregnant are expelled from school.[2]

Contraception

* There is general knowledge about contraception among youths, but little practical information and much misinformation about side effects hinder the use of modern contraceptives.[2]
* Culture and religious beliefs prohibit the use of contraception.[3]
* Government is reluctant to teach adolescents about contraception, or provide it to unmarried women.[3]
* An estimated 39% of married women report using contraception; with about a third using modern methods.[4]
* Only 12% of Kenyan men currently use condoms.[6]

Abortion

* Abortion is illegal unless the mother's life is at risk.[6]
* Abortion is not an uncommon experience, especially among young, single, urban women.[6]
* While few statistics are available on the overall rate of women seeking abortions in Kenya, reports maintain that one-third of maternal deaths are due to illegal, unsafe abortions. Of the total number of women treated for complications of illegal abortion, about 60% are under the age of 24.[4]

Sex Education

* In the absence of traditional sources of information, young people turn to their peers for information concerning issues relating to sex.[2]
* Many schools are run by religious orders, and the government opposes sex education in the school.[3]

Sexually Transmitted Infections (including HIV)

* An estimated 1.2 million people were living with HIV/AIDS in Kenya at the end of 2001.[7]
* As is the case in many African countries, HIV prevalence in Kenya is higher among women than among men.[7]
* AIDS is more prevalent among higher paid workers because of traveling to big cities to find work.[5]
* Youth are largely aware of STIs including HIV/AIDS but often misinformed on modes of transmission and which diseases are actually sexually transmitted.[2]
* Kenya requires HIV testing for couples wishing to get married.[7]

Sexual Orientation[8]

* Sections 162 to 165 of the Penal Code criminalize homosexual behavior and attempted homosexual behavior between men, referring to it as "carnal knowledge against the order of nature". The penalty is 5 to 14 years' imprisonment. Lesbian relations are not mentioned in the law.
* Kenyan law defines any sexual relations between men as a criminal act. There are, however, few prosecutions; one exception is a 1998 investigation into the Forum for Positive Generation on AIDS Prevention, a registered community organization for people with HIV

in Kisumu. Police alleged that the organization has been "recruiting" homosexuals.

Prostitution

❖ Young men frequent prostitutes, often for their first sexual encounter.[2]

❖ In an economy with too few jobs, single women without education are turning to prostitution.[9]

❖ A great number of women in the cities who have been abandoned by men or in need of extra income also turn to prostitution.[9]

Pornography

❖ All forms of erotica and sexually oriented publications are illegal in Kenya, and not available for sale. This includes publications featuring nudity, which is culturally offensive.[10]

Resources

▶ Family Planning Association of Kenya, Family Health Plaza, Junction Mbagathi Langata Roads (Nairobi West) P.O. Box 30581-00100 Nairobi. Tel: (254 20) 603923/27 or 604296/7.

▶ International Planned Parenthood Federation-Africa Region, Box 30234, Nairobi, Kenya. Tel: 254-2/720280.

MEXICO

**MEXICO
(UNITED MEXICAN STATES)**
POPULATION: 107,449,525

CAPITAL: MEXICO CITY
POPULATION: 19,013,000

Major Cities:	Mexico City, Guadalajara, Puebla
Ethnic Groups:	Mestizo 60%, Amerindian 30%, White 9%
Languages:	Spanish (official) and Mayan dialects
Major Religions:	Roman Catholic 89%, Protestant 6%
GDP per capita (PPP):	$10,000
Urban Population:	74%
Infant Mortality:	20 per 1,000 live births
Life Expectancy:	Females: 78 years; Males: 73 years
Adult Literacy:	92%
Health Care System:	Social welfare; 1 doctor per 1,000 persons.

References
❑ *The World Almanac and Book of Facts* (2006). NY: World Almanac Education Group.
❑ *The World Factbook* http://www.cia.gov/cia/publications/factbook/ Accessed June 25, 2006.
❑ *World Reference Atlas* (2005). NY: Dorling Kindersley Publishing.

Sexual Activity

❖ The legal age of consent is 12 for hetero-sexuals, and 18 for homosexuals.[1]

❖ The average age of women at first birth is 21.[2]

Contraception

❖ In Mexico, where the government provides contraceptive services and methods free of charge, public-sector family planning services meet the contraceptive needs of 72% of the population.[3]

❖ Mexican law provides that maternal and infant health care and family planning are to be considered basic health services, and the former is considered a priority. The family planning laws and policies are outlined in the Mexican Regulation on Family Planning Services35 and in the Reproductive Health and Family Planning Program 1995–2000.[4]

❖ The family planning services provided by the government include information, orientation, counseling, selection, prescription, and distribution of contraceptive methods. These services and the contraceptive methods are free of charge. In particular, public services provide oral hormonal methods, injectable methods, IUDs, sterilization, vasectomy, barrier methods, and spermicides.[4]

❖ Emergency contraception is available over-the-counter.[4]

❖ The General Health Law establishes that family planning services are a priority within the general provision of health services. The objectives of the family planning subprogram are: to strengthen and broaden the coverage and quality of family planning information, education and services, with special emphasis on rural areas; to contribute to a decrease in fertility; to reduce the number of unwanted, unplanned and high-risk pregnancies; and to broaden activities designed to diversify the use of modern contraceptive methods.[4]

❖ According to the government, in 1995, 67% of women of childbearing age who lived with their partner used some method of family planning. The best-known modern contraceptive methods are: the birth control pill, female sterilization, the intrauterine device (IUD), and traditional methods.[4]

❖ The prevalence of contraceptive use among women between the ages of 15 and 19 increased from 14% in 1976 to 36% in 1992. The most commonly used methods are: hormonal methods (40%), the intrauterine device (34%), and barrier methods (9%).[4]

❖ In Mexico, surgical sterilization is the most common family planning method and has a prevalence rate of 43% among women of childbearing age. However, research has revealed that one-fourth of sterilized women claimed not to have been informed of the irreversible nature of the operation, or of alternative contraceptive methods available at the time; 39% claimed not to have signed the consent form.[4]

Abortion

❖ The Decree of 2 January 1931, as amended 16 February 1971, makes abortion illegal except in cases of medical or legal grounds to save the life of the woman or in cases of rape or incest. Some interpretations allow abortion in order to preserve the physical health of the woman, although this interpretation varies from state to state.[5]

❖ Most abortions are performed during the first trimester. They must be performed by a physician with the corroboration of another physician as to the necessity of the procedure. The consent of the woman and her husband (or in the case of teens, a parent or guardian) is required.[5]

❖ The abortion laws in Mexico are less harsh than in other Latin American countries, but abortion continues to be illegal in most cases. Women of means can have safe abortions, while poor women have to resort to clandestine abortions in extremely unsafe conditions.[4]

❖ The estimated total number of induced abortions in Mexico is 850,000 per year whereas the total number of abortions in Mexico (including miscarriages and induced abortions) is 1.7 million per year.[4]

❖ Abortion is the third or fourth greatest cause of death in Mexico.[4]

❖ Abortion ranges from the second to the fourth greatest reason for hospitalization in Mexico. The Ministry of Health's facilities attend 50,000 cases of complications following abortions every year.[4]

Sex Education

❖ It is the government's policy to stabilize population growth. To that end, the Population Law of January 1974 gave power to the Secretary of Government to implement family planning by means of education and services to the public, while the Sanitary Code of 1973 (Sec. 34) provides for family planning in schools.[6]

❖ In general, Mexican adolescents receive information about contraception too late, and they tend to receive sex education that emphasizes biological facts over decision-making skills.[7]

❖ The majority of young people in Mexico confront the risks of sexual relations with little information and a great deal of mystification. They receive little or no advice as to how to deal with their sexuality in a responsible way; they have poor knowledge about reproductive health; and they have only limited access to contraceptive services and methods. However, despite the obvious need for urgent action, programs to improve

young people's sexual and reproductive health are the subject of controversy long before they are introduced. A small number of conservative groups that have significant influence in Mexico are always present in the debate, censoring everything from the content of chapters on sexual education in government textbooks to messages about safe sex in the press. These groups advocate sexual abstinence, no sex outside of marriage and the withholding of information about contraception from young people so as to "alienate" them from sex.[4]

Sexually Transmitted Infections (including HIV)

❖ Although adult HIV prevalence remains low in Mexico (0.3%), an estimated 180,000 people were living with HIV in 2005—as many as two thirds of them were men who are believed to have been infected during sex with other men.[8]

❖ There are signs that heterosexual transmission of HIV is increasing as more women are infected by their partners who also have sex with men.[8]

❖ Thirteen percent of these cases of HIV/AIDS were women. Blood transfusions are the most common means of transmission for women, representing 56.5% of the AIDS cases in adult women. Sexual transmission is the means of infection in four out of every ten cases of women with AIDS. In 1995, it was estimated that the prevalence of HIV in pregnant women was one of every 3,000 cases, and that every year, 500 HIV-positive women become pregnant.[4]

Sexual Orientation[9]

❖ The Mexican Constitution states that men and women are equal. Education should promote the ideals of "fraternity and equal rights of all mankind, avoiding privileges of race, sects, groups, sexes or individuals." This law is not effectively enforced. Amnesty International cites Mexico homosexual men and women to be the most likely victims of abuse and violence.

❖ Beginning Oct. 1,1999 Penal Code Article 281 prohibited discrimination "based on age, sex, pregnancy, marital status, race, language, religion, ideology, sexual orientation, skin color, nationality, social origin or position, work or profession, economic status, physical features or health." The penalty for violation of the law is one to three years in prison and/or a fine equal to 50 to 200 days' salary and/or 25 to 100 days of community service. The law prohibits provocation or incitement of hate or violence, and bans bias in employment and public accommodations and services.

Prostitution[10]

❖ Larger cities have "zona roja" where prostitution is allowed. Prostitutes are registered, get health checks and must carry a card to prove it.

❖ Cab drivers know the locations of prostitutes and will drive customers to those locations and wait for them.

Pornography[10]

❖ The hardest pornography openly available is equivalent to *Hustler* or *Penthouse*.

❖ Video stores carry pornographic movies, but don't display the boxes.

❖ It is illegal to sell or show a child under 18 years of age pornography.

Resources

▶ Fundacion Mexican Para la Planeacion Familiar (MEXFAM), Juarez 208, Tlalpan, 14000 Mexico City, DF, Mexico. Tel: (52-55) 5487-0030. Website: *http://www.mexfam.org.mx/*

▶ National AIDS Committee, Secretary for Health, Lieja Numero 7, Col. Juarez, 1er Piso, 04360 Mexico City, DF, Mexico. Tel: (5) 554-9112.

▶ International Gay and Lesbian Association-Mexico (Associacion Lesbia y Gay Internacional-Mexico), Apartado Postal 1 1693, 06030 Mexico City, DF, Mexico.

▶ Academy of Human Rights, Apartado Postal 78282, CD Universitaria, 04510, Mexico City, DF, Mexico.

NETHERLANDS

Major Cities:	Amsterdam, Rotterdam, The Hague
Ethnic Groups:	Dutch 83%
Languages:	Dutch (official), Frisian (official)
Major Religions:	Roman Catholic 31%, Dutch reformed 13%, Calvinist 7%, Muslim 6%
GDP per capita (PPP):	$30,500
Urban Population:	89%
Infant mortality:	4 per 1,000 births
Life Expectancy:	Females: 82 years; Males: 76 years
Adult Literacy:	100%
Health Care System:	Hospitals and private physicians; 1 doctor per 400 persons.

References
- *The World Almanac and Book of Facts* (2006). NY: World Almanac Education Group.
- *The World Factbook* http://www.cia.gov/cia/publications/factbook/ Accessed June 25, 2006.
- *World Reference Atlas* (2005). NY: Dorling Kindersley Publishing.

Sexual Activity

❖ Legal age of consent for sex is 16. However, Dutch law permits a young person between 12 and 16 to have sexual relationships as long as the young person consents.[1]

❖ Most Dutch teens begin their sexual career with "French" kissing and huggling at around age 14 [2]

❖ Half of 18–19 year olds have experienced sexual intercourse.[2]

Contraception

❖ Young people in the Netherlands have a high level of effective contraceptive use. Nearly 85% use contraception at first intercourse. Pill use is extremely high "Double Dutch"—the use of the Pill and condom together for protection from pregnancy and diseases—is used by 24% of those who are sexually active.[2]

❖ Oral contraception, as well as other 'medical' methods of contraception have been available free of charge in The Netherlands since 1972. Condoms are not funded.[3]

❖ Emergency contraception, commonly known as "the morning after pill," has been available since the 1960's.[4]

Abortion

❖ The Netherlands has one of the lowest abortion rates in Europe.[5]

❖ Abortion is available for free on demand if the woman is 16 or older and is in a situation of emergency.[6]

❖ Consultation with a doctor followed by a five-day waiting period is necessary before an abortion is performed.[6]

❖ Abortion is permitted up to the 22 weeks, almost all abortions are performed before the 8th week of pregnancy.[6]

❖ RU-486 (Mifepristone) was approved for marketing in 1999.[7]

Sex Education[2]

❖ Sexuality education typically begins at home with parents.

❖ Sex education in schools is not compulsory. However, since 1993 some compulsory core objectives, for both primary and secondary education, have been put into place.

❖ Sexuality education is focused on encouraging young people to gain autonomy in their own attitudes and behavior regarding sexuality. It gives young people not only the medical and health knowledge, but also the skills to negotiate relationships and understand emotional as well as physical side of sexuality.

❖ Sex education is also available through youth clubs, evening classes for adults and is also covered by the mass media.

Sexually Transmitted Infections (including HIV)

❖ An estimated 19,000 people were living with HIV/AIDS at the end of 2003.[8]

❖ HIV testing is systematic for blood donors and for some insurance applicants.[8]

❖ From 2004 universal screening in pregnant women in the Netherlands started.[8]

❖ From January 1st 2002, a registration is coordinated by the HIV Monitoring Foundation in Amsterdam and is based on the 22 HIV/AIDS treatment centers in the Netherlands.[8]

❖ The "Double Dutch" campaign gave a double message: use a condom to prevent disease and the Pill to prevent pregnancy. This approach was promoted when AIDS first became a major issue in the late 1980s.[2]

Sexual Orientation

❖ The Dutch Penal Code bans discrimination on the basis of "hetero- or homosexual orientation." Article One of the

Constitution also prohibits discrimination based on sexual orientation. The Equal Treatment Commission provides redress from discrimination in work-, education- and service-related situations.[9]

❖ On April 1, 2001 The Netherlands became the first country in the world to offer same-sex couples the freedom to marry, providing gay and lesbian people the full range of protections, responsibilities, and benefits that come with civil marriage, including adoption.[10]

❖ There are no remaining anti-lesbian or anti-gay provisions in Dutch Criminal law. Until 1971, lesbian and gay sex between an adult and a minor (meaning under 21) was an offence. Today, the legal age of consent is 16 years for lesbians, gays and straights.[11]

❖ In 1974, there was an abolition of the ban on gays in the military.[12]

Prostitution[13]

❖ Prostitution is legal, and in 2000 brothels also became legal for the first time since 1912. The intention of the new law is to turn "sex work" into just another job, complete with employment rights and even a trade union. There is no evidence that prostitution has increased as a result: indeed the famous red-light district in Amsterdam is, if anything, smaller than it once was.

❖ Most prostitutes seem to dislike their new legal status, because it has forced them to pay taxes, and it has made it easier for the police to drive illegal immigrants out of the business. But they also admit that the Netherlands has done more than most to separate organized crime from sex work.

❖ Prostitutes must be at least 18; clients must be at least 16. Violation of either age limit is a crime for the other party.

❖ Window prostitution is the most visible form, though only takes up about 20% of the entire sex industry in the Netherlands.

Pornography[14]

❖ The Netherlands has very liberal laws. Pornography is sold openly at normal newsstands.

❖ Material involving animals declared illegal in 2006 due to new animal-welfare laws.

Resources

▶ Rutgers Nisso Group, Oudenoord 176–178, 3513 EV Utrecht, The Netherlands. Tel: 31 30 231 34 32. Website: *http://www.rutgersnissogroep.nl/*

▶ The Netherlands Institute for Health Promotion and Disease Prevention (NIGZ), De Bleek 13, Postbus 500, 3440 AM Woerden, The Netherlands.

NEW ZEALAND

NEW ZEALAND

POPULATION: 4,076,140

CAPITAL: **WELLINGTON**

POPULATION: 342,500

Major Cities:	Auckland, Wellington, Christchurch
Ethnic Groups:	New Zealand European 70%, Maori 8%, Asian 6%, Pacific islander 4%
Languages:	English (official), Maori (official)
Major Religions:	Anglican 24%, Roman Catholic 15%
GDP per capita (PPP):	$25,200
Urban Population:	89%
Infant Mortality:	6 per 1,000 births
Life Expectancy:	Females: 82 years; Males: 76 years
Adult Literacy:	100%
Health Care System:	70% publicly funded, with private physicians and clinics bridging gap in waiting for services; midwifery subsidized; 1 doctor per 504 persons.

References

❑ *The World Almanac and Book of Facts* (2006). NY: World Almanac Education Group.
❑ *The World Factbook* http://www.cia.gov/cia/publications/factbook/ Accessed June 25, 2006.
❑ *World Reference Atlas* (2005). NY: Dorling Kindersley Publishing.

Sexual Activity

❖ Age for sexual consent is 16 years old.[1]

❖ The rising rate of teen pregnancy is a growing public issue.[2]

Contraception

❖ Age of consent for medical treatment is as low as 14 in parts of New Zealand.[3]

❖ In an effort to lower New Zealand's abortion rate, the government offers free birth control pills to women.[4]

❖ The Pill and female sterilization are the most popular methods.[5]

❖ Emergency contraception is available over-the-counter in New Zealand.[6]

Abortion

❖ Abortion is available to women in their first trimester, from regular physicians in licensed institutions. The procedure is free if performed at a public hospital. After the first trimester, abortions are available within an institution with "full license," and with the approval of a committee of three: two certifying physicians, one of which is an OB/GYN, and the operating surgeon. Counseling of the mother is a prerequisite.[2]

❖ Abortions can be obtained in order to save the woman's life, to preserve the physical or mental health of the mother, in cases of rape or incest, fetal impairment or for economic or social reasons.[2]

❖ RU-486 (Mifepristone) is available for early abortion in New Zealand.[7]

Sex Education

❖ The FPA of new Zealand launched 'The Word—on sex, life and relationships' a multi-media awareness campaign to provide young people aged 12–15, with information about relationships, sexuality and sexual health. The Word involved radio advertising, a free telephone information line and a free booklet. Twelve thousand calls were received within the first week. Young people say that the word is straight to the point, easy to read and that they particularly like the dictionary contained in the booklet.[8]

❖ A major study in New Zealand showed that teaching safer sex using tactics of fear, monogamy or abstinence increased the incidence of unsafe sex in high-risk individuals and so increased the spread of HIV. The study also found that anti-discrimination legislation, and teaching of tolerance of homosexuality, helped decrease the spread of AIDS.[9]

Sexually Transmitted Infections (including HIV)

❖ Annual, new diagnoses in New Zealand have more than doubled since 1999—from fewer than 80 to 183 in 2005—but national adult HIV prevalence remains very low at under 0.2%. Much of the recent trend is attributable to an increase in HIV diagnoses among men who have sex with men.[10]

❖ The first AIDS cases in New Zealand were reported in 1983.[10]

❖ The refugee component for the HIV total for 2000 was small, compared to previous years. While refugees accounted for 40% of cases in 1998 (the peak year) they accounted for only 17% of cases in 2000.[10]

❖ In 1993, a law was passed which bans discrimination because of the presence of disease, including HIV and Hepatitis.[11]

Sexual Orientation

❖ The New Zealand Human Rights Act includes protection based on sexual orientation in employment, education, access to public places, provision of goods and services, and housing and accommodation.[12]

❖ Homosexual Law Reform Act became law in 1986. It was an Act to amend the Crimes Act 1961 by removing criminal sanctions against consensual homosexual conduct between males, and by consequentially amending the law relating to consensual anal intercourse. In effect, consenting adult gay (male) sexual behavior was decriminalized and the age of adult consent was changed to sixteen years, equating to the age of consent for heterosexual sexual behavior.[13]

❖ The New Zealand Bill of Rights Act of 1990 provides that everyone has the right to freedom from discrimination on grounds which include sex, marital status, family status, and sexual orientation.[13]

❖ New Zealand's parliament passed legislation to recognize civil unions between gay couples. The Civil Union Bill also recognizes unions between men and women who do not want to marry. The new law took effect April 2005, and gives unmarried couples the same rights as married couples in areas like child custody, tax and welfare.[14]

Prostitution[15]

❖ Prostitution is legal.

❖ In June 2003, a bill was passed in Parliament that legalized prostitution, pimping and brothel-keeping. Brothel keepers must apply for an operator's license although this is formality unless the person has a serious criminal conviction.

Pornography[16]

❖ The Films, Videos and Publications Act of 1993 covers publications of all types (audio/visual, written, or computerized). The legislation calls for levels of classification: unrestricted is labeled green and is available to anyone; unrestricted with a yellow label is available only to certain ages; restricted is given a red label and is available to certain ages; objectionable "describes, depicts or otherwise deals with matters such as sex, horror, crime, cruelty or violence. . . to be injurious to the public good."

Resource

▶ New Zealand Family Planning Association (NZPFA), Dixon House, Castrol Street, Wellington, NZ. Tel: (4) 384-4349.

NORWAY

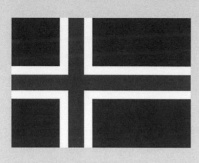

NORWAY

POPULATION: 4,610,820

CAPITAL: OSLO
POPULATION: 791,500

Major Cities:	Oslo, Bergen, Trondheim, Stavanger
Ethnic Groups:	Norwegian, Sami
Languages:	Norwegian (official)
Major Religions:	Church of Norway 86%, Pentecostal 1%, Roman Catholic 1%, other Christian 2%
GDP per capita (PPP):	$42,300
Urban Population:	75%
Infant Mortality:	4 per 1,000 births
Life Expectancy:	Females: 82 years; Males: 77 years
Adult Literacy:	100%
Health Care System:	1 doctor per 313 persons.

References
❏ *The World Almanac and Book of Facts* (2006). NY: World Almanac Education Group.
❏ *The World Factbook* http://www.cia.gov/cia/publications/factbook/ Accessed June 25, 2006.
❏ *World Reference Atlas* (2005). NY: Dorling Kindersley Publishing.

Sexual Activity

❖ Legal age of consent for heterosexual relations is 16.[1]

❖ Nearly 60% of young women surveyed said they began having sex before age 18.[2]

Contraception

❖ Sterilization has become one of the most common forms of birth control for married men and women over the age of thirty.[3]

❖ Approximately 10,000 men and women are sterilized each year.[3]

❖ The overall use of condoms in Norway suggests that they are used more for birth control than as a means to protect against sexually transmitted infections.[3]

❖ The government fully supports family planning, domestically and internationally, and services are provided in Maternal and Child clinics and other health outlets free-of charge. All contraceptives are widely available, and contraceptive use is high.[4]

❖ Emergency contraception is available over-the-counter.[5]

Abortion

❖ In January of 1979, a law was passed to make abortion legal up to twelve weeks gestation.[6]

❖ After twelve weeks, a board of doctors makes the decision whether or not to abort the fetus.[6]

❖ The legalization of abortion did not increase the rate of abortions from 1974 to 1984. After 1985, the abortion rate did increase somewhat.[6]

❖ Illegal abortions are rare in Norway, but if a woman has been refused a second trimester abortion, she may travel to another country to have one.[6]

❖ Minors must obtain written parental consent.[2]

❖ RU-486 (Mifepristone) was approved for marketing in 2000.[7]

Sex Education[4]

❖ The Norwegian Association for Sexuality and Reproductive Health, produce a regular newsletter. They also conduct research on adolescent sexual, contraceptive and abortion behavior, as well as providing sex education seminars.

Sexually Transmitted Infections (including HIV)[8]

❖ An estimated 2,100 people were living with HIV/AIDS in Norway at the end of 2003.

❖ HIV testing is systematic for blood donors, pregnant women (including women having abortions) and STI patients.

❖ Diagnosed HIV cases are reported in a national HIV database using an identifying code.

❖ In 2003, 238 new cases of HIV were reported. This is the highest incidence in recent years and is primarily caused by an increase of cases among MSM and a continuously high rate of infection among heterosexuals originating from a country with a generalized HIV epidemic. (59% of the new HIV cases were among non-Norwegian nationals).

Sexual Orientation

❖ Homosexuality is accepted in Norway; same-sex partnerships are recognized.[9]

❖ There is no discrimination of homosexuals in the military.[10]

❖ Laws prohibiting discrimination on the grounds of sexual orientation were introduced in 1981:

◆ S.349a of the Penal Code makes it an offence "in business or similar activities" to refuse to give goods or services (on the conditions applicable to others) to a person because of his or her "homosexual inclination, lifestyle, or orientation." The offence can be punished with fines, or with imprisonment of up to six months.

♦ Under S.135a of the Penal Code it is unlawful "to publicly threaten or deride, or to incite to hatred, persecution or contempt" against a person or group on account of their "homosexual inclination, lifestyle, or orientation." The penalty is a fine, or imprisonment up to a maximum of two years.[10]

❖ Foreign partners of lesbian women and gay men can be granted residence rights on proof of a long-term relationship.[11]

Prostitution[12]

❖ Prostitution is legal in Norway; but laws exist that can be used against prostitutes or clients of prostitutes. One of these is the prohibition against soliciting.

❖ Pimping and procuring are illegal.

❖ PION is the Norwegian prostitutes' rights organization.

❖ Oslo has about 2,000 prostitutes working mostly on the streets and in massage parlors.

Pornography

❖ Hardcore material is illegal to produce, distribute and sell, but legal to possess. One may acquire it abroad, on the Internet, or via satellite TV. There are also some illegal porn shops, especially in the larger cities. To satisfy legal requirements, editors of erotic magazines, domestic TV channels and cable TV have obscured *sexual organs in activity* using black rectangles etc. After the Supreme Court in December 2005 unanimously acquitted a former magazine editor for publishing unobscured hardcore pornography in 2002, however, it is understood that printed hardcore pornography is no longer illegal, and it is expected that pornographic magazines will be introduced in general stores.[13]

❖ The Norwegian National Criminal Police is considered among the leading law enforcement agencies in the world when it comes to investigation, intelligence and technological equipment to combat child pornography and abuse on the Internet.[14]

Resource

▶ Norwegian Association for Sexual and Reproductive Health (NSSR), RFSU Norge AS, Kirkegt. 5, 0152 Oslo, Norway. Tel: 47 (99) 35 92 73. Website: *http://www.nsrr.org/*

POLAND

POLAND
POPULATION: 38,536,869

CAPITAL: WARSAW
POPULATION: 2,201,900

Major Cities:	Warsaw, Lodz, Krakow
Ethnic Groups:	Polish 97%
Languages:	Polish (official) 98%
Major Religions:	Roman Catholic 90%
GDP per capita (PPP):	$13,300
Urban Population:	65%
Infant Mortality:	7 per 1,000 births
Life Expectancy:	Females: 79 years; Males: 71 years
Adult Literacy:	99%
Health Care System:	Hospitals, private physicians; 1 doctor per 450 persons.

References
- ❏ *The World Almanac and Book of Facts* (2006). NY: World Almanac Education Group.
- ❏ *The World Factbook* http://www.cia.gov/cia/publications/factbook/ Accessed June 25, 2006.
- ❏ *World Reference Atlas* (2005). NY: Dorling Kindersley Publishing.

Sexual Activity

❖ Legal age of consent for sex is15.[1]
❖ Only 12% of young women surveyed said they began having sex before age 18.[2]

Contraception

❖ Contraception use is low due to the lack of availability.[3]
❖ 80% of women claim that they use contraception; the methods chosen are withdrawal or rhythm rather than the Pill or IUD.[3]
❖ Heavy church influences have caused pharmacists to give up stocking effective contraceptives.[3]
❖ In Poland, sterilization as a method of family planning is illegal. Even with the written consent of the patient, sterilization is considered a criminal injury, which carries a penalty of up to 10 years in prison. Sterilization is legal only when performed upon "mentally incompetent individuals.[4]

Abortion

❖ In Poland, a liberalizing abortion law adopted in 1996 was invalidated by the Constitutional Court in 1997. The Court found that the law, which permitted abortion on social and economic grounds, violated the Constitution's protection of the right to life of the "conceived child." In December 1997, Poland's Parliament enacted new legislation eliminating social and economic grounds for abortion.[4]
❖ Currently, abortion in Poland is available on three grounds: when the pregnancy threatens the life or health of the woman; when there is justified suspicion that the pregnancy resulted from a "criminal act;" and in instances of fetal impairment.[4]
❖ The legal abortion rate is currently near zero as a consequence of new restrictions. Nevertheless, many Poles reportedly seek abortion services in nearby countries or from illegal providers in Poland.[5]
❖ The Federation for Women and Family Planning estimates there are at least 200,000 illegal abortions carried out annually.[6]

Sex Education[7]

❖ Sex education in Poland has been compulsory since 1972.
❖ In 1994 a law obligated the government to provide sexuality education in schools.
❖ A book completed by the Board of Education: *Preparing for Family Life*, was met with opposition from sex educators due to its content supporting the church's view on abortion and contraception use.

Sexually Transmitted Infections (including HIV)[8]

❖ By April 2004, 8.760 HIV infections have been reported. Most of the infections are seen in Warsaw, Gdansk region and Katowice (south).
❖ Injecting drug users account for the majority (5,050, or 58 percent) of all reported HIV cases in Poland.
❖ IDU are systematically screened in treatment centers, outpatient clinics and residential homes. All other groups are tested on a voluntary basis.
❖ Diagnosed HIV infected cases are registered in a national HIV database using the name for identification, excluding those testing anonymously. A switch to anonymous reporting is being planned.
❖ Nationwide, levels of reported STIs have been stable and relatively low in the recent years. However in some western regions of Poland there is an observed increase in STIs levels. Prostitution has substantially increased at borders of Poland and Czech and German borders; levels of STIs in those areas have increased as well.

* In a survey of homosexual men, very few reported having had an HIV test. In addition there is still stigma associated with homosexuality, reflected in the low number of those voluntarily identifying themselves as homo/bisexual; the number of infections in this subpopulation may therefore be underestimated.

Sexual Orientation[9]

* In April 1995 the Constitutional Committee of the Polish Parliament proposed that the anti-discrimination clause of the constitution include protection from discrimination on the grounds sexual orientation. However this proposal met strong opposition, particularly from the Roman Catholic Church. The constitution as finally approved by Parliament in March 1997 dropped the list of protected categories of people, the revised anti-discrimination article reading as follows: "Nobody can be discriminated based on any ground in political, social or economical life.

* Homosexuality was decriminalized in 1932, establishing an equal age of consent of 15 years regardless of the sexual orientation.

* Article 18 of the Polish Constitution (1997) restricts marriage to heterosexual couples: "The marriage is a relationship between woman and man, the family, motherhood and parenthood are under protection and care of Republic of Poland." That does not mean it forbids registered partnership between the people of the same sex, but certainly defines marriage as a heterosexual one.

Prostitution[10]

* Prostitution is completely unregulated, and legal.

Pornography[11]

* Illegal, although posters and calendars of naked women are available.

* Pornographic films are distributed by video clubs.

Resource

▶ Poland Family Planning Association: Towarzystwo Rozwoju Rodziny (TRR) ul. Scwerynów 4, 0039 Warsaw, Poland. Tel: 48 (22) 828 61 91/92. Website: *http://www.trr.org.pl/*

PORTUGAL

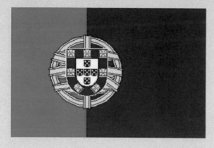

PORTUGAL
POPULATION: 10,605,870

CAPITAL: LISBON
POPULATION: 2,618,100

Major Cities:	Lisbon, Porto
Ethnic Groups:	Homogeneous Mediterranean stock, small African minority
Languages:	Portuguese (official), Mirandese (official)
Major Religions:	Roman Catholic 94%
GDP per capita (PPP):	$19,300
Urban Population:	63%
Infant Mortality:	5 per 1,000 live births
Life Expectancy:	Females: 81 years; Males: 74 years
Adult Literacy:	93%
Health Care System:	National Health Services and private hospitals; 1 doctor per 345 people.

References
❑ *The World Almanac and Book of Facts* (2006). NY: World Almanac Education Group.
❑ *The World Factbook* http://www.cia.gov/cia/publications/factbook/ Accessed June 25, 2006.
❑ *World Reference Atlas* (2005). NY: Dorling Kindersley Publishing.

Sexual Activity

❖ Age of consent for heterosexual intercourse is 14, while homosexual sex is 16.[1]

❖ One quarter (26%) of young women surveyed said they began having sex before age 18.[2]

Contraception

❖ Safe contraception is not widespread.[3]

❖ Oral Contraceptives are sold in pharmacies without medical prescription.[3]

❖ Emergency contraception is available over-the-counter.[4]

Abortion

❖ Under current law a woman can have an abortion only if her life is in danger, to protect her mental or physical health, or in cases of rape, incest or fetal impairment.[5]

❖ The restrictive abortion legislation in Portugal leaves many women who want to end an unwanted pregnancy with the only option of back street abortion. Such restrictive legislation results in more women traveling to neighboring countries, or resorting to illegal abortion in Portugal, risking, not only prosecution, but their lives and their health.[5]

❖ Since the eighties around 100 women died in Portugal because of illegal abortion. Every year about 1000 Portuguese women are treated in hospitals because of post-abortion complications or incomplete abortions.[5]

❖ Majority of abortions are still performed illegally by doctors, nurses, midwives and private clinics.[3]

Sex Education

❖ The law passed in 1984 gave the right to sex education and family planning in the school curriculum.[6]

❖ In 1999, the government organized—for the first time—an inter-ministerial commission with the aim of producing a governmental program on sex education and family planning. This commission was integrated by the Health Ministry, the Education Ministry, the Justice Ministry and the Labor and Social Solidarity Ministry. In October 1999 this program was launched—the first time that any Portuguese government has had a public program on these matters.[7]

Sexually Transmitted Infections (including HIV)

❖ About 24,000 people were living with HIV/AIDS in Portugal at the end of 2003.[8]

❖ Trend analysis of surveillance data reflects the diversity of the HIV/AIDS situation in the country, but young adults are most affected.[8]

❖ Prior to 2000 Portugal did not report HIV cases so analysis of the HIV epidemic is difficult.[8]

❖ Portugal has the highest HIV incidence rates in Western Europe, with injecting drug use accounting for almost 50% of HIV diagnoses in 2002.[9]

Sexual Orientation

❖ Article 71 of the Penal Code which ban's "acts against nature" has been used against lesbian women and gay men. Other legislation has been used to deny lesbian and gay parents custody of their children after divorce.[10]

❖ Homosexuality as an illness was dropped from scientific writings in 1979.[10]

❖ There are no anti-discrimination laws in the penal code covering gays and lesbians. Extensive lobbying was conducted in 1996 during the revision of the Constitution in favor of the inclusion of "sexual orientation" in its Article 13 which lists the non-discrimination categories and points out groups within society specially prone to discrimination, i.e., sex, race, religion, etc. The Portuguese lesbian and gay association presented a formal proposal to Parliament. The Green Party made a similar proposal. Both were rejected by the Socialist and Social Democrat majority. [11]

❖ Lesbians and gay are banned from serving in the Armed Forces and police force. [11]

❖ The Portuguese parliament approved a registered partnership law, but limited to heterosexuals, not same-sex relations. [11]

❖ During 1997 several major events irreversibly changed the Portuguese lesbian and gay community and gave it a degree of visibility not previously achieved. These included the first AIDS Candlelight Memorial March, the first Pride Festival, the first Gay and Lesbian Film Festival and the opening of the first gay and lesbian community centre. [11]

Prostitution[12]

❖ Prostitution was legal in Portugal until 1994.

❖ Opinion towards prostitution is ambiguous, different attitudes towards female, male and child varies greatly. Female prostitution is tolerated while male and child prostitution is not accepted and is much more hidden.

Pornography[12]

❖ The legal age for viewing pornography in Portugal is 18.

Resource

▶ Associacao Para o Planeamento da Familia (APF), 38 Rua Artilharia um 2DT, 1250-040 Lisbon, Portugal. Tel: (351 21) 385 39 93. Website: *http://www.apf.pt/*

ROMANIA

ROMANIA

POPULATION: 22,303,552

CAPITAL: BUCHAREST

POPULATION: 2,210,800

Major Cities:	Bucharest, Constana
Ethnic Groups:	Romanian 90%, Hungarian 7%, Roma 3%
Languages:	Romanian (official), Hungarian, German
Major Religions:	Eastern Orthodox 87%, Protestant 8%, Roman Catholic 5%
GDP per capita (PPP):	$8,200
Urban Population:	56%
Infant Mortality:	26 per 1,000 births
Life Expectancy:	Females: 75 years; Males: 68 years
Adult Literacy:	98%
Health Care System:	1 doctor per 540 persons.

References

❑ *The World Almanac and Book of Facts* (2006). NY: World Almanac Education Group.
❑ *The World Factbook* http://www.cia.gov/cia/publications/factbook/ Accessed June 25, 2006.
❑ *World Reference Atlas* (2005). NY: Dorling Kindersley Publishing.

Sexual Activity

❖ Age of consent for sex is 14.[1]

Contraception[2]

❖ Modern contraceptives are only sporadically available at a cost similar to abortion.

❖ Reproductive services are mostly controlled by underpaid state-employed gynecologists.

❖ Due to the lack of modern contraceptives, fears of their side effects and limited access to family planning services, women tend to rely on natural methods of birth control and abortion.

❖ Percentage of types of contraception used: Withdrawal: 25%, Rhythm: 6%; Condom: 3%; IUD: 3%; Pill: 2%; Tubal Ligation: 1%; Spermicides: 0.5%; No Method: 59%.

Abortion

❖ Abortion was legally available from 1957 to 1966, then was severely restricted as part of an overall pronatalist policy. As illegal and unsafe abortions replaced legal procedures, abortion-related mortality rose steeply, reaching a record-high level of 142 deaths for every 100,000 live births in 1989; just one year later, when most restrictions were removed, the rate fell to about one third its peak level.[3]

❖ As of 1989 the new government of Romania abolished the law that prohibited abortions. This led to a surge in legally performed abortions from 109,819 in 1989 to 913,973 in 1990.[4]

❖ In 1991 the rate abortions women were having was three abortions to every one birth.[4]

❖ Many Romanian women accept abortions as a primary form of contraception due to their misconceptions about other forms of birth control.[4]

Sex Education[4]

❖ Sex education was removed from the school system in the early 1980's.

❖ Few efforts to introduce sex and contraception education into the secondary schools have been met with opposition from teachers and parents.

❖ The major sources of contraception and sex information: Friend (45%), Mass media (19%), Health care providers (10%).

Sexually Transmitted Infections (including HIV)[5]

❖ Between 5,500–14,000 people were living with HIV/AIDS in Romania at the end of 2004.

❖ Most probably, Romania has the highest number of HIV infections in the sub-region of Central and South Eastern Europe.

❖ In 1989 a dramatic epidemic of HIV infection was discovered among orphans and hospitalized children who contracted HIV through blood transfusions.

❖ HIV testing is mandatory for STI and TB patients, pregnant women and prostitutes.

❖ Since 1994–1995, there has been a steady increase in the HIV/AIDS incidence rate among adults mainly related to the sexual and injected drug use transmission of the virus. This correlates with the growing incidence of STIs (syphilis in particular).

❖ Data on diagnosed HIV cases are reported at national level since 1992.

Sexual Orientation[6]

❖ Until November 14, 1996 same-sex relationships in Romania were illegal under Article 200 of the penal code. On that date Article 200 was amended so that the complete ban was lifted, but replaced with provisions that were almost as oppressive and discriminatory. Little real progress had been achieved.

❖ Homosexuality is legal except in cases where it causes a "public scandal," involves a minor, a defenseless person, or if it is by coercion or rape; up to five years in prison.

❖ Today in Romania, gays and lesbians are routinely denied some of the most basic human rights guaranteed by international law. Despite amendments in 1996 to the criminal code provisions relating to homosexual conduct—portrayed by the Romanian government as a total repeal of legislation criminalizing consensual sexual relations between adults of the same sex—gays and lesbians continue to be arrested and convicted for such relations if they become public knowledge. Moreover, they face frequent physical abuse and harassment by law enforcement officials, as well as systematic discrimination in many walks of life. Romanian law not only prohibits private sexual acts between consenting adults of the same sex, but may also be interpreted to punish speech and association that expresses a homosexual identity—or even support of such identity.

❖ Homosexual propaganda and proselytism are banned.

Prostitution[7]

❖ Child prostitution is a problem due to the large number of unwanted children. Under dictator Nicolae Ceausescu, abortion was illegal, contraceptives unavailable and sex education non-existent.

Pornography

❖ No information found.

Resource

▶ Society for Education in Contraception & Sexuality (SECS), Str Dimitrie Bacovita Nr 3 B, 023991 Bucharest—Sector 2, Romania.

Tel: 40 (21) 310 33 13. Website: http://www.sexdex.ro/

RUSSIAN FEDERATION

RUSSIAN FEDERATION

POPULATION: 142,893,540

CAPITAL: **Moscow**
POPULATION: 10,672,000

Major Cities:	Moscow, St. Petersburg, Nizhniy Novgorod, Novosibirsk
Ethnic Groups:	Russian 80%, Tatar 4%, Ukranian 2%
Languages:	Russian (official), many others
Major Religions:	Russian Orthodox 15–20%, Muslim 10–15%
GDP per capita (PPP):	$11,100
Urban Population:	77%
Infant Mortality:	15 per 1,000 births
Life Expectancy:	Females: 74 years; Males: 60 years
Adult Literacy:	99%
Health Care System:	1 doctor per 220 people.

References

❑ *The World Almanac and Book of Facts* (2006). NY: World Almanac Education Group.
❑ *The World Factbook* http://www.cia.gov/cia/publications/factbook/ Accessed June 25, 2006.
❑ *World Reference Atlas* (2005). NY: Dorling Kindersley Publishing.

Sexual Activity

❖ The legal age of consent is 16.[1]

❖ Premarital sexual relations in the Russian Federation are more widespread than ever before, indicating that the age at which people are having sexual intercourse has decreased.[2]

❖ Sexual activity before marriage is typical for the majority of today's youth: 79% of young married women and 75% of young married men have had sexual intercourse before marriage.[2]

❖ The average age of first intercourse for girls is now 16.[3]

Contraception

❖ Abortion had been the main method of birth control because of the lack of choices.[4]

❖ A 1998 study found that 69%–78% of sexually active women reported using a contraceptive method. The majority (51%–60%) said they used modern contraceptives like the IUD and Pill. The IUD was by far the most popular contraceptive among the women.[5]

❖ Emergency Contraception is available: Postinor is packaged in a 4-pill strip with directions for women to take one tablet immediately after intercourse, but to use no more than four tablets per month.[6]

Abortion

❖ The Russian Federation was the world's first country to legalize abortion. In 1920 the Communist Party legalized abortion in an attempt to destroy the traditional family and religion, and to create a new social basis for Russian Communist society. However, in 1936 the law was repealed and abortion was illegal. Abortion became legal again in 1955.[7]

❖ A decree issued in 2003 restricts the circumstances under which women may legally obtain abortions from the end of the 12th week until the beginning of the 22nd week of pregnancy. The decree reduces from 12 to 4 the number of conditions under which abortion is legal during this period.[8]

❖ Illegal abortion is still common; the number of illegal abortions is thought to equal the number of legal abortions.[7]

❖ The Russian Federation ranks second in the world to Romania in the number of abortions per capita. Girls in Russia (under 18) account for every tenth abortion. About 60% of all pregnancies in the Russian Federation end in abortion.[9]

❖ On average every woman born in Russia has two or three abortions.[5]

❖ RU-486 (Mifepristone) is available in Russia.[10]

Sex Education[11]

❖ Sex education does not exist in the school curriculum. The Family Planning Association is the main agency involved in sex education.

❖ The majority of Russians are supportive of sexuality education in schools.

❖ The federal program entitled "Principles of Family Planning and a Healthy Way of Life" for adolescents—developed by the Russian Family Planning Association and approved by the Minister of General and Professional Education and the Ministry of Health—was banned and deprived of funding as a result of political uproar. Opponents of sex education argued that sex education and the dissemination of contraceptives would corrupt and exterminate the Russian people.

Sexually Transmitted Infections (including HIV)[12]

❖ About 900,000 people were living with HIV/AIDS in the Russian Federation at the end of 2004.

❖ The Russian Federation has the biggest AIDS epidemic in all of Europe.

- Until 1995, HIV/AIDS surveillance was organized mostly through mandatory screening in most subgroups of the population, together with contact tracing. Since then, testing has remained mandatory only for blood donors, prisoners and professionals exposed to HIV.
- The number of tests done has decreased by 43% between 1994 and 1996, due in part to the change in testing policies and reduced funding; there was a decrease of 33% and 54% among blood donors and prisoners for whom testing policies remained the same.
- Diagnosed HIV infections are reported by name in a national HIV case reporting system.
- Incidence of syphilis cases increased dramatically from < 30 cases per 100,000 in 1978–92 to 172 per 100,000 in 1995.
- Incidence of gonorrhea cases increased from 75 cases per 100,000 in 1987 to 236 cases per 100,000 in 1993 and then decreased to 165 cases per 100,000 in 1995; underreporting of gonorrhea is estimated to be substantial.

Sexual Orientation

- In 1993 the Russian Parliament enacted a new penal code which no longer includes the prohibition of homosexuality. Until 1993 consensual anal intercourse between adult males was punishable under Article 121.1 of the Russian Federation criminal code by imprisonment of up to five years. Lesbian relations were not criminalized.[13]
- Negative attitudes about homosexuality persist: One poll found that 23 percent of Russians believed that homosexuals should be executed, 32 percent said they should be isolated; only 12 percent said they should be left in peace.[14]

Prostitution

- In 1987, the Supreme Soviet of the Russian Republic made prostitution an administrative offense punishable by fines up to 200 rubles ($360).[15]
- The Soviet attempt to eradicate prostitution in the 1920s (by encouraging female employment, job-training, and government clinics and housing) is still considered more progressive than the alternatives used in countries around the world today of regulation, prosecution, or decriminalization.[16]

Pornography

- The collapse of communism in the former USSR brought about a resurgence of commercially available sexually explicit materials. The problem became so acute that Prime Minister Mikhail Gorbachev had to appoint a committee to suggest measures to safeguard Russian morality.[17]
- Moscow authorities banned the sale of highly profitable erotic material on the Russian capital's streets and in transit stations. To protect children from pornography, which was rare in the former Soviet Union until the mid 1980s, the city council restricted sales of adult publications to designated shops and ordered sexually explicit materials wrapped in plastic to prevent perusal by minors. It also made illegal the sale of pornography to and by anyone under 16.[18]

Resources

▶ Russian Family Planning Association, 18/20 Vadkovsky per., 101479 Moscow Russia. Tel: 7 (495) 973 15 59. Website: http://www.rfpa.ru/

▶ Russian Sexological Association, Krylatskiye Kholmy, 30–2, 207 Moscow.

SINGAPORE

SINGAPORE

POPULATION: 4,492,150

CAPITAL: SINGAPORE

POPULATION: 3,438,600

Major Cities:	Singapore
Ethnic Groups:	Chinese 77%, Malay 14%, Indian 8%
Languages:	Mandarin 35%, English 235%, Malay 14%, Hokkien 11%, Cantonese 6%, Teochew 5%. Tamill 3%
Major Religions:	Buddhist 43%, Muslim 15%, Christian 10%, Taoist 9%, Catholic 5%, Hindu 4%
GDP per capita (PPP):	$28,100
Urban Population:	100%
Infant Mortality:	2 per 1,000 live births
Life Expectancy:	Females: 84 years; Males: 79 years
Adult Literacy:	93%
Health Care System:	One of the highest health standards in Southeast Asia; 1 doctor per 693 persons.

References
❏ *The World Almanac and Book of Facts* (2006). NY: World Almanac Education Group.
❏ *The World Factbook* http://www.cia.gov/cia/publications/factbook/ Accessed June 25, 2006.
❏ *World Reference Atlas* (2005). NY: Dorling Kindersley Publishing.

Sexual Activity

❖ The legal age of consent for heterosexual sex is 14; homosexual sex is illegal.[1]

❖ In the early 1970's, Singapore attempted to reduce its population through national programs, including financial incentive for sterilization. By 1984, this was working too well, and by 1987, the birth shortfall was judged to be detrimental to the country. Sterilization incentives were no longer available to better-educated families, although it was retained for less-educated families, as well as those with three or more children. Three children were seen as the optimal family size. Advertising reflected this view.[2]

❖ Lee Kuan Yew, Singapore's founding leader suggested that polygamy may be a solution to one of Singapore's major problems: better educated women are less likely to marry and procreate, leaving the less educated women to have the majority of Singapore's offspring.[3]

Contraception

❖ The government, as part of its national development program, embarked on a family planning program immediately after Singapore achieved full independence in 1965. Besides the comprehensive provision of clinic services, the program included a wide range of social and fiscal incentives to achieve a "two child" family norm. After a decade of below replacement fertility, the government replaced the policy in 1987 with a selectively pro-natalist "three or more if you can afford it" policy.[4]

❖ Contraceptive services are readily available to the whole population through services provided by the Ministry of Health, public and private doctors.[4]

❖ About 60% of married couples report using some method of birth control. Condoms are the most common method used, followed by sterilization. The Pill and IUD are not popular methods.[5]

Abortion[6]

❖ Abortion was legalized in 1970, and was completely liberalized in 1975. This has led to the abolition of criminal abortions, allowing any woman access to a safer procedure.

❖ Ninety-five percent of all abortions are performed before the 13th week of pregnancy.

❖ Seventy-two percent of all abortions are performed on married women.

❖ Abortion ends about one third of all pregnancies in Singapore.

Sex Education

❖ The Singapore Planned Parenthood Association has an established formal sex education program in schools and also provides sex education for out-of-school youth.[4]

❖ A government program started in 2001, teaches sex and sexuality in school to 11-to-18-year-olds. Teenagers in secondary school discuss kissing in public, having sex, homosexuality, getting pregnant, pornography, and the dangers of sexually transmitted infection. Sexual harassment is also among the issues older teens discuss.[7]

❖ Mindful of differing views on sexuality, the government consulted major religious groups, as well as teachers, parents, students, psychologists and counselors before beginning the program. While students are given the facts on underage sex and homosexuality, they are also told that these are against the law.[7]

Sexually Transmitted Infections (including HIV)[8]

❖ An estimated 2,100 people were living with HIV/AIDS in Singapore at the end of 2001.

❖ HIV testing among sex workers has been conducted in Singapore since 1985. However, no evidence of HIV infection was found among this group until 1992, when 0.8 per cent of sex workers were tested positive. In 2000, the prevalence of HIV infection among sex workers screened was 0.7 per cent.

Sexual Orientation

* Homosexuality is outlawed in Singapore [3]
* Two sections of the Singapore Penal Code criminalize homosexual acts:
* Section 377 (Unnatural Offences): "Whoever voluntarily has carnal intercourse against the order of nature with any man, woman or animal, shall be punished with imprisonment for life, or with imprisonment for a term which may extend to ten years, and shall also be liable to fine. Penetration is sufficient to constitute the carnal intercourse necessary to the offence in this section."
* Section 377A (Outrages on Decency): "Any male person who, in public or private, commits, or abets the commission by any male person, of any act of gross indecency with another male person, shall be punished with imprisonment for a term which may extend to two years." Both sections carry a mandatory punishment of jail. [9]
* Visual representation of homosexual acts is banned, and so are materials that portray homosexuality as a legitimate and acceptable lifestyle. [9]

Prostitution [10]

* Prostitution is legal, but operating a brothel and public soliciting are not. In Designated Red-light Areas (DRAs), it is officially tolerated.
* Working women must carry a yellow card stating that they are registered and have recently had a health exam.
* Some brothels provide benefits to keep employees.
* Prostitutes do not tend to work because of financial necessity, since there is no poverty and nearly full employment in Singapore.

Pornography [10]

* It is legal to view pornography on the Internet, but illegal to download it.
* Sexually explicit material is censored by the Ministry of Information and the Arts.
* Laws prohibit pornography, including "sexual perversions" such as homosexuality on the Internet.
* A Government-appointed panel determines what is banned from books, magazines, public, films, newspapers, etc. in Singapore.

Resource

▶ Singapore Planned Parenthood Association, 03–04 Pek Chuan Bldg., 116 Lavender St., Singapore, 1233.

SLOVAKIA

SLOVAKIA
POPULATION: 5,439,448

CAPITAL: **BRATISLAVA**
POPULATION: 428,800

Major Cities:	Bratislava, Kosice
Ethnic Groups:	Slovak 86%, Hungarian 10%, Roma 2%
Languages:	Slovak (official) 84%, Hungarian 11%
Major Religions:	Roman Catholic 69%, Protestant 11%, Greek Catholic 4%
GDP per capita (PPP):	$16,100
Urban Population:	57%
Infant Mortality:	7 per 1,000 births
Life Expectancy:	Females: 79 years; Males: 71 years
Adult Literacy:	100%
Health Care System:	State health insurance, high immunization rates; 1 doctor per 290 persons.

References
❏ *The World Almanac and Book of Facts* (2006). NY: World Almanac Education Group.
❏ *The World Factbook* http://www.cia.gov/cia/publications/factbook/ Accessed June 25, 2006.
❏ *World Reference Atlas* (2005). NY: Dorling Kindersley Publishing.

Sexual Activity

❖ Age of consent for sexual activity is 15.[1]

Contraception

❖ Due to the lack of use of reliable contraception methods, abortion has been the most reliable family planning practice.[2]

❖ Only 28% of women at risk for unplanned pregnancy use modern contraceptives.[2]

❖ Gynecologists view condoms as somewhat convenient, and only somewhat reliable against pregnancy and disease.[2]

❖ There is a relatively restrictive law on voluntary sterilization.[3]

❖ Only 6% of at-risk women were using hormonal contraception, 13% used IUDs, and 5% had been sterilized, according to the first national contraceptive prevalence survey.[3]

❖ The Slovak Family Planning Association is attempting to improve the public's knowledge about contraception, and to change negative attitudes.[3]

❖ The Slovak Family Planning Association is also attempting to introduce legislation on voluntary sterilization.[3]

❖ Postinor, an emergency contraceptive from Hungary, is registered in Slovakia.[4]

Abortion[5]

❖ Abortion is available on request up to 12 weeks.

❖ It is also available in the second trimester for medical reasons, risk to the mother or the fetus, or for rape and other sexual crimes.

❖ There must be at least 6 months between abortions, with the exception of women with at least two births, aged 35 or more, or in the case of rape.

❖ Recommendation of physician is needed.

❖ Parental consent is required for minors under the age of 16; for women aged 16–18, a physician must inform parents after abortion.

❖ Counseling is required.

Sex Education

❖ Some sex education subjects exist in school curricula, under the title of Family Life Education.[6]

❖ Family Planning Association considers these programs to be conservative.[6]

❖ Family Planning Association is the main agency involved in sex education.[6]

❖ Sex education activities include lectures to parents and youth.[6]

❖ Family Planning Association provides educational materials.[6]

❖ Slovakia's high abortion rate is attributed to inadequacies in school sex education.[3]

❖ Slovakia's Family Planning Association is working to influence public opinion about such topics through the use of mass media, and they are trying to create a comprehensive planned parenthood network.[3]

❖ Collection of statistical data must be completed.[3]

❖ The Slovak Family Planning Association and the Slovak Woman's Social Democracy Community are working to form a sex education curriculum for school children.[3]

❖ Problems with such programs include a lack of available resources published in Slovak, moral support, lack of international standards and human rights education.[3]

Sexually Transmitted Infections (including HIV)[7]

❖ An estimated 180 people were living with HIV/AIDS in Slovakia at the end of 2003.

❖ Well-designed national HIV/AIDS program are thought to have contributed to low prevalence among IDUs and low incidence in non-injecting populations. A syringe exchange program has been operating in Bratislava since 1994. The low prevalence of HIV in IDUs in the city is attributed to the success of the program.

❖ There has been a slow, but persistent increase of HIV + cases, mostly in MSM and heterosexuals.

❖ HIV is predominantly transmitted through homo/bisexual sex.

❖ In the last few years there has been an increase in syphilis. The number of reported cases increased from 0.6 to 5.2 per 100,000 population; in majority cases of new infections of syphilis. In the years 1995–99, 38 cases of congenital syphilis were registered.

❖ The number of gonorrhea cases seem to be decreasing. In 1980, 3168 cases were registered; in 1999, only 108 cases were reported. It is more than probable that this situation is connected to improved access to antibiotics and self-treatment.

Sexual Orientation[8]

❖ The latest legal change of the Penal Code concerning homosexual behavior came in 1990 (Law 175/1990), when homosexuality and heterosexuality were treated equally. Paragraph 244 was excluded from the Penal Code, the age of consent became 15 years for homosexual and heterosexual behavior, and homosexual prostitution was no longer regulated by the criminal law.

❖ There are no anti-discrimination laws to protect gays and lesbians... a constitutional list of human rights and freedoms was accepted by the Czechoslovak Parliament in 1991 (Law 23/1991). Deputy Klara Samkova wanted "sexual orientation" to be added to the list, but this was not approved by the majority of Parliament.

❖ A draft law that would give homosexuals in long-term relationships the status of "registered partners" has been ready since 1997, but was not approved by the cabinet or the current government. The law would allow homosexual partners, among other things, to refuse to testify in court against their mate, to take three days off work in the event of their partner's death, and to deed property to each other without taxation.

Prostitution[9]

❖ Prostitution is larger and more organized than it was in 1989, at the end of Soviet rule.

❖ Recently, entrepreneurs have opened massage parlors in Slovakia. Prostitutes generally have 'bodyguards' to bring them to and from clients.

❖ Inconsistent legislation allows the use of legal business premises for sexual services.

❖ The general feeling about prostitution is negative, and this attitude shows in a quote by Slovakian Interior Ministry member Tibor Shellberger: "We can say that prostitution today has become a very advantageous branch of international organized crime."

Pornography[9]

❖ In 1995, Slovakia began allowing private television on VTV Cable. The Company will not broadcast programs with erotic scenes, pornography, violence and brutality.

Resource

▶ Slovak Association for Family Planning and Parenthood Education, Palisady 44, Bratislava. 811 06, Slovak Republic. Tel: 421

(2) 54 43 08 89. Website: *http://www.rodicovstvo.sk/*

SOUTH AFRICA

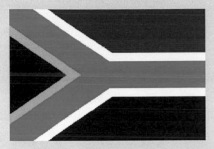

SOUTH AFRICA
POPULATION: 44,187,637

CAPITAL: **PRETORIA**
POPULATION: 1,541,300

Major Cities:	Cape Town, Johannesburg, Pretoria
Ethnic Groups:	Black African 79%, White 10%, Colored 9%
Languages:	11 official languages including: IsiZulu, IsiXhosa, Sepedi, English, Setswanai, Sesotho, Xitsonja
Major Religions:	Zion Christian 11%, Pentacostal 8%, Catholic 7%, Methodist 7%, Dutch 7%, Anglican 4%
GDP per capita (PPP):	$12,000
Urban Population:	50%
Infant Mortality:	61 per 1,000 births
Life Expectancy:	Females: 42 years; Males: 43 years
Adult Literacy:	86%
Health Care System:	Private clinics, government supported programs; 1 doctor per 1,750 people.

References

❑ *The World Almanac and Book of Facts* (2006). NY: World Almanac Education Group.
❑ *The World Factbook* http://www.cia.gov/cia/publications/factbook/ Accessed June 25, 2006.
❑ *World Reference Atlas* (2005). NY: Dorling Kindersley Publishing.

Sexual Activity

* Legal age of consent is 16 for heterosexuals and 19 for homosexuals.[1]
* The typical age of first intercourse: 16 years old.[2]
* Polygyny (multiple wives) is practiced by 15–30% of married men.[2]
* The Contraceptive Prevalence Survey found that 1 woman out of 7 women had their first pregnancy while in school.[2]
* Sexual activity is more in the open now that apartheid is abolished.[3]

Contraception

* In 1932, the government founded the Family Planning Association; it has 5,000 mobile sites that provide people with information and contraceptives.[4]
* The most common methods of contraception by race are: Whites: Pill (21%); Blacks: Injection (26%); Colored: Injection (27%); Indian: Sterilization (25%).[4]
* Family Planning services are free of charge to all races.[4]
* Emergency contraception is not widely used; it is only given to 100 patients annually.[5]

Abortion

* South Africa enacted the Choice on Termination of Pregnancy Act in 1996, making its abortion law one of the most liberal in the world. The Act permits abortion without limitation as to reason during the first 12 weeks of pregnancy, within 20 weeks on numerous grounds and at any time if there is risk to the woman's life or of severe fetal impairment. The Act repealed a 1975 law that had prohibited abortion unless the pregnancy was a result of rape or incest, the mother's life was in danger, or there was a fetal impairment.[5]
* Legalization reduced the adverse consequences of unsafe abortion: Six months after legal abortion became available in February 1997, the number of incomplete abortions at one large hospital in Port Elizabeth had declined from an average of 18 every week to approximately four.[7]
* RU-486 (Mifepristone) is available for use in South Africa.[8]

Sex Education

* The Population Development Program educates people about contraception.[4]
* According to the African National Congress Policy Guidelines for a Democratic South Africa, sex education and family planning will be included as part of a future national health program.[4]
* Since a new constitution has been made which protects free speech, sex in magazines and films is legal. Sex education will be required in schools in the near future.[3]
* Even though 1-in-nine South Africans are living with HIV/AIDS, the country's large-scale prevention programs (including information campaigns and condom distribution efforts) appear to be bearing fruit. In recent surveys, about 55% of sexually active teenage girls report they always used condoms during sex.[9]

Sexually Transmitted Infections (including HIV)

* South Africa's epidemic is one of the worst in the world. Almost one in three pregnant women attending public antenatal clinics were living with HIV in 2004 and trends show a gradual increase in HIV prevalence. There has been significant scale-up on the treatment front—around 190,000 people were receiving therapy by the end of 2005—however this still only represents less than 20% of those in need.[9]
* Nearly a million children have been orphaned by AIDS.[9]

* An estimated 5.5 million people (18.8% of adults) were living with HIV/AIDS in South Africa at the end of 2005.[10]
* In 2000, 11 million STI episodes were reported.[10]

Sexual Orientation

* The South African Constitution includes sexual orientation as a protected category.[11]
* On 8th May 1996 South Africa became the first country in the world to enshrine lesbian and gay rights in its Constitution: Clause 9 reads: "The state may not unfairly discriminate directly or indirectly against anyone on one or more grounds, including race, gender, sex, pregnancy, marital status, ethnic or social origin, color, sexual orientation, age, disability, religion, conscience, belief, culture, language, and birth." A similar provision had previously been included in the Interim Constitution adopted in December 1993. The ANC had formally recognized lesbian and gay rights as part of its policy at its conference in May 1992.[12]
* In January 2000 the South African national assembly approved a bill that outlaws discrimination on grounds such as race, gender, religion and disability in a bid to eradicate the lingering inequalities of the apartheid era. The Promotion of Equality and Prevention of Unfair Discrimination Bill contains a wide-ranging list of 17 grounds on which no person may be discriminated against. These include sexual orientation, age, culture, pregnancy, marital status, conscience, social standing and language.

Though already enshrined in the country's liberal 1996 constitution, they can now be enforced through every court in the country and replace the old regime's racist laws which were wiped off the statute books nearly a decade ago.[12]

Prostitution[13]

* The law (and society) has adopted an ambivalent attitude towards prostitution. On the one hand prostitution is universally condemned as a social evil and the prostitute is condemned and penalized for the manner in which he or she carries on their profession. On the other hand, prostitution is tolerated to the extent that it is not forbidden to be a prostitute and the prostitute's customers are allowed to enjoy the prostitute's services with impunity.

Pornography

* Pornography is illegal, but the government doesn't enforce the law.[14]
* In 1994, pictures of women's breast couldn't be published without covering her nipples. However, today explicit magazines showing women's breast are made available in supermarkets.[14]
* South Africa has a comprehensive definition of child pornography that addresses explicitly its manifestations on the Internet. The Films and Publications Act No. 34 of 1999 and 2004 states: "Child pornography includes any image, however created, or any description of a person, real or simulated, who is, or who is depicted or described as being, under the age of 18 years.[15]

Resource

▶ Planned Parenthood Association of South Africa, Third Floor, Marlborough House, 60 Eloff, Johannesburg, So. Africa, 2001

SPAIN

SPAIN

POPULATION: 40,397,842

CAPITAL: MADRID
POPULATION: 5,130,000

Major Cities:	Madrid, Barcelona, Valencia, Serville, Zaragoza
Ethnic Groups:	Mix of Mediterranean and Nordic types
Languages:	Castilian Spanish (official) 74%, Catalan 17%, Galician 7%, Basque 2%
Major Religions:	Roman Catholic 94%
GDP per capita (PPP):	$25,500
Urban Population:	77%
Infant Mortality:	4 per 1,000 births
Life Expectancy:	Females: 83 years; Males: 76 years
Adult Literacy:	98%
Health Care System:	1 doctor per 244 persons.

References

❏ *The World Almanac and Book of Facts* (2006). NY: World Almanac Education Group.
❏ *The World Factbook* http://www.cia.gov/cia/publications/factbook/ Accessed June 25, 2006.
❏ *World Reference Atlas* (2005). NY: Dorling Kindersley Publishing.

Sexual Activity

❖ Legal age of consent for heterosexual and homosexual relations is 12; this is the lowest age of consent in Europe.[1]

❖ Typical age of first intercourse: 16.5 years old.[2]

❖ According to one study, almost 30% of 15–19 year olds have had first sexual intercourse in an "at-risk" situation: either because they were not using any method of contraception or because the methods they were using were inadequate.[2]

Contraception

❖ Contraceptive use was officially legalized in 1978.[3]

❖ Most common methods of contraception: Barrier (14%), Pill (12%), IUD (8%); 16% report no method.[3]

❖ Emergency contraception is available without consulting a doctor or having a prescription.[4]

❖ Due to the high rate of unprotected sex among adolescents (despite availability of contraceptives), emergency contraception is in high demand. For example, one family planning clinic for youth found that 25% of clients contact the clinic for this method.[4]

Abortion

❖ Since 1985, abortion has been legally permitted on limited grounds: when the pregnancy presents a serious risk to the mother, rape (up to 12 weeks), and fetal abnormalities (up to 22 weeks).[5]

❖ Efforts to liberalize abortion (e.g., allow abortion on request until the 12th week) have been made.[6]

❖ Most abortions (95%) are carried out in private clinics where women pay for the abortion themselves (35,000-60,000 pesetas or US$350–600).[7]

❖ RU-486 (mifepristone) was approved for marketing in 1999.[8]

Sex Education[2]

❖ The Ministry of Social Affairs subsidized the opening of three Youth Contraception and Sexuality Centers (in Barcelona, Santiago, and Madrid) to educate youth about contraception and sexuality issues.

❖ Once a taboo subject, sexuality is now present on television, in cinema and in magazines, and it has been included in official education programs.

❖ In 1990, the Law of General Arrangement of the Education System was passed which included to need to provide sex education as part of health education.

Sexually Transmitted Infections (including HIV)

❖ An estimated 140,000 people were living with HIV/AIDS in Spain at the end of 2003.[9]

❖ Spain does not report national HIV data, since HIV case reporting only exists in some regions. Data from those regions show that during the 1980s HIV spread widely among large numbers of injection drug users and, to a much lesser extent, homosexual men. The larger number of sexually active young adults among the HIV infected injecting drug users led to sexual transmission to non-injecting sexual partners and to children through mother to child transmission.

❖ By the start of the 1990s more than 100,000 HIV infections had already occurred and AIDS-related mortality ranked first among the major causes of potential years of life lost in Spain. In the 1990s intensified targeted interventions led to marked reductions in new HIV infections in injection drug users, homosexual men and women who engaged in sex work.

❖ A significant share of HIV infections (24%) is occurring via heterosexual transmission. But injecting drug use is the main mode of transmission. Reported HIV prevalence among injecting drug users in 2000 was 20–30% nationwide.[10]

Sexual Orientation

❖ The Spanish Penal Code declares the right to express one's sexual orientation as a fundamental freedom and bans discrimination based on sexual orientation in housing, employment, public services, and professional activities. It also criminalizes hatred and violent acts against individuals based on their sexual orientation.[11]

❖ This Penal Code is one of the most advanced in penalizing discrimination based on sexual orientation, and the first to protect the rights of homosexuals in a Latin Catholic country.[12]

❖ The Spanish parliament approved a new law in 2005 which allows same sex marriages and adoptions.[13]

Prostitution[14]

❖ Prostitution itself is legal, but several surrounding activities are not. Brothels were outlawed in 1956, but they live on in the form of "Clubs."

Pornography[14]

❖ Pornography is sold openly in most book stands; zoophily and S/M material is legal like in the Netherlands.

Resources

▶ Federacion de Planificacion Familiar de Espana, Ponce de Leon, 8, 1° - 1, 28010 Madrid Spain. Tel: 34 (91) 591 34 49. Website: *http://www.fpfe.org/*

▶ Federacion Espanola de Sociedades de Sexologia, c/Valencians, 6-Principal, 46002, Valencia.

▶ Societat Catalan de Sexologia, Tren de Baix, 51, 20, 20, 08223 Teraessa, Barcelona.

▶ Sociedad Sexologica de Madrid, c/Barbieri, 33 dcha, 28004, Madrid.

SWEDEN

SWEDEN
POPULATION: 9,016,596

CAPITAL: **STOCKHOLM**
POPULATION: 1,622,300

Major Cities:	Stockholm, Goteborg, Malmo, Uppsala
Ethnic Groups:	Swedish 89%, Finnish 2%
Languages:	Swedish (official)
Major Religions:	Lutheran 87%
GDP per capita (PPP):	$29,800
Urban Population:	83%
Infant Mortality:	3 per 1,000 births
Life Expectancy:	Females: 83 years; Males: 78 years
Adult Literacy:	100%
Health Care System:	Physicians: 1 per 355 persons.

References
- ❑ *The World Almanac and Book of Facts* (2006). NY: World Almanac Education Group.
- ❑ *The World Factbook* http://www.cia.gov/cia/publications/factbook/ Accessed June 25, 2006.
- ❑ *World Reference Atlas* (2005). NY: Dorling Kindersley Publishing.

Sexual Activity

❖ Legal age of consent for sex is 15 for all.[1]
❖ Sweden has very liberal attitudes towards teenage sexuality.[2]
❖ There are no parental rights when it comes to the sexuality of minor women, except below the age of 15. A young Swedish woman can independently decide whether she wants to have a boyfriend, have sex with him, have contraceptives or even have an abortion.[2]
❖ The typical age of first intercourse is 16.[3]

Contraception

❖ Contraception was legalized in 1938.[4]
❖ Contraceptives are easily accessible, affordable and available to anyone, regardless of age or marital status. Such accessibility has proven effective in the prevention of teen pregnancy. For example, only 35 babies were born to mothers under 16 in 1993.[2]
❖ Permission from parents, other guardian or husband is not needed, and there are no religious prohibitions against contraceptives.[2]
❖ Youth Clinics in every community offer free, confidential services and counseling in sexual matters to young people.[2]
❖ Midwives provide about 80% of all contraceptive counseling.[5]
❖ Anyone who is over 25 and a Swedish citizen or legal resident can be sterilized on request.[4]
❖ Birth control pills are free for the first 3 months.[6]
❖ Since 1990, the RFSU clinic has advocated emergency contraception by offering the service and information to both professionals and the general public.[5]
❖ Emergency contraception is marketed under various names by Schering AG as a four-pill strip with its own package insert.[7]

Abortion

❖ Sweden has one of the lowest numbers of abortions in the world.[2]
❖ Available on request up to 12 weeks on consultation with a doctor, between 12 and 18 weeks on consultation with a doctor and a counselor, and after 18 weeks with the approval of the National Board of Health and Welfare.[4]
❖ Abortion is free.[6]
❖ Rates of abortion have remained stable (and low) since 1980.[8]
❖ RU 486 (Mifepristone) has been available since 1992.[9]
❖ More then half (51%) of abortions performed within 63 days of a woman's last menstrual period use Mifepristone/RU 486.[10]

Sex Education

❖ Sex education has been a compulsory subject in Swedish schools since 1955. Sex education starts at the age of seven, in the first grade, and then is brought up on a recurring basis for approximately 15 hours per year.[2]
❖ Swedish children receive their first sex education at home, from their parents.[11]
❖ Sex education is well integrated in school curricula.[12]
❖ Swedish sex education has been based on the principles of democracy, tolerance, and human equality. Ethical principles of Swedish sex education include: (a) Nobody is entitled to regard and treat another human being simply as a means of selfish gratification, (b) Mental pressure and physical force are always a violation of individual liberty, and (c) Sexuality forming part of a personal relationship has more to offer than casual sex and is therefore worth aspiring to. This, it will be observed, does not imply any moral castigation of persons dependent on casual sexual relations during periods of their lives. Nearly all young

persons take the view that sexual fidelity towards a person with whom one has a personal relationship with is a duty. Schools should support this conviction.[13]

Sexually Transmitted Infections (including HIV)

❖ An estimated 6,300 people were living with HIV/AIDS in Sweden at the end of 2003.[14]

❖ HIV testing is mandatory for blood donors and systematic but voluntary for pregnant women, women having abortions, IDU, STI patients, immigrants, refugees and deceased with autopsies.[14]

❖ All diagnosed HIV infections are registered in the Swedish national HIV case reporting system, using an identifying code.[14]

❖ During the 1990s the Swedish HIV-epidemic has been influenced by the global epidemic. People who have been infected outside Sweden, usually in countries with a generalized epidemic, contribute 2/3 of the reported cases in recent years. The majority of this group has been infected prior to their immigration to Sweden.[14]

❖ Prevalence in pregnant women and STI patients is primarily generated through the national testing programs.[14]

❖ In 2003 there was a continued increase in registered STI cases. 596 new cases of gonorrhea (an increase of 18 percent compared to 2002 and the highest number of cases in ten years), 26,802 new cases of chlamydia (a 9 percent increase compared to 2002 and also the highest number of cases since 1989) and 179 new cases of syphilis (an increase of 40 percent compared to 2002 and the highest number of cases in 20 years.).[14]

❖ Sweden has a very successful STI program which provides free STI diagnosis and treatment, partner notification, sex education in schools, publicity about high gonorrhea rates and condom promotion.[2]

Sexual Orientation

❖ The Partnership Act was passed through the Riksdag in 1994. This means that homosexual couples that contract a partnership with each other have broadly the same rights as heterosexual couples who contract a marriage with each other. There are some exceptions, for example, homosexual couples are not allowed to adopt children.[15]

❖ The Swedish Federation for Gay and Lesbian Rights reports that more and more lesbian women are conceiving children through self-insemination with sperm donated from a gay male friend, and with joint custody of the child.[4]

❖ Sweden has no policy excluding persons who engage in homosexual behavior from military service.[16]

Prostitution

❖ In Sweden it is legal to sell sex, but it is illegal to be a pimp and since 1999 also to buy sexual services. The reason for this law is to protect prostitutes, as many of them have been forced into prostitution by someone or by economic necessity. Prostitutes are generally viewed by the government as oppressed, while their clients are viewed as oppressors.[17]

Pornography

❖ In Sweden, the possession of child pornography is forbidden but it is not forbidden to "watch". Possession of child pornography is only illegal if movies or pictures with child pornography are downloaded and saved in the hard drive, floppy disk or CD-ROM. Watching child pornography on the Internet by saving the link under "favorites" or under the so-called "cyber hard drives" is not considered illegal according to Swedish law.[18]

Resources

▶ Swedish Association for Sex Education (RFSU), P.O. Box 12128, Drottningholmsvagen 37, Stockholm 102 24 Sweden. Tel: (46 8) 692 07 00. Website: *http://www.rfsu.se/*

▶ National Institute of Public Health, SE-103 52 Stockholm Sweden. Tel: (46 8) 566-135-00.

SWITZERLAND

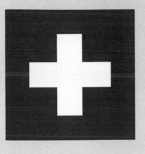

SWITZERLAND
POPULATION: 7,523,934

CAPITAL: BERN
POPULATION: 122,700

Major Cities:	Zurich, Basel, Geneva, Lausanne
Ethnic Groups:	German 65%, French 18%, Italian 10%, Romansch 1%
Languages:	German 64%, French 20%, Italian 7% (all official)
Major Religions:	Roman Catholic 42%, Protestant 35%
GDP per capita (PPP):	$32,300
Urban Population:	68%
Infant Mortality:	4 per 1,000 births
Life Expectancy:	Females: 83 years; Males: 78 years
Adult Literacy:	100%
Health Care System:	Excellent, major producer of specialized pharmaceutical products; 1 doctor per 333 persons.

References
❏ *The World Almanac and Book of Facts* (2006). NY: World Almanac Education Group.
❏ *The World Factbook* http://www.cia.gov/cia/publications/factbook/ Accessed June 25, 2006.
❏ *World Reference Atlas* (2005). NY: Dorling Kindersley Publishing.

Sexual Activity

- ❖ Age of consent in Switzerland is 16.[1]
- ❖ Nearly 40% of women surveyed said they began having sex before age 18.[2]
- ❖ The age of first intercourse is essentially the same as other European countries.[3]
- ❖ Switzerland has one of the lowest teen pregnancy rates. This seems to be the result of widespread Swiss school sexuality education programs and a nationwide AIDS campaign that has stressed the use of condoms in sexual activities.[3]

Contraception[4]

- ❖ High school students were the one's who requested condom availability in schools.
- ❖ There are numerous family planning centers throughout the country, some for counseling only, but others offering gynecological exams and contraception.
- ❖ Adolescents can easily obtain birth control.

Abortion

- ❖ Abortion has been legal since 1942.[4]
- ❖ In June 2002, the Swiss public voted for abortion on request of the woman within the first 12 weeks of pregnancy.[5]
- ❖ Before an abortion is performed the doctor have to inform and counsel the woman and give her the addresses of specialized counseling centers where she can receive more information and help.[5]
- ❖ Young women under the age of 16 have to visit a counseling centre before an abortion can be performed.[5]
- ❖ The costs of the abortion is covered by health insurance.[5]
- ❖ There are regional differences in availability of services.[4]
- ❖ RU-486 (Mifepristone) was approved for marketing in 1999.[6]

Sex Education

- ❖ Switzerland has a long history of school-based sex education.[3]
- ❖ The Swiss Foundation for Sexual and Reproductive Health focuses on information, education and advocacy for sexual and reproductive health care and rights. The Foundation has been has been involved in a Parliamentary Advocacy Program, and has undertaken activities such as sending questionnaires to all parliamentary candidates, seeking their views on sex education and a budget for development cooperation.[5]
- ❖ The Stop AIDS Campaign attempts to provide AIDS education through the use of billboards and television ads discussing condom use, as well as through a soft-porn video demonstrating the use of condoms.[7]

Sexually Transmitted Infections (including HIV)[8]

- ❖ An estimated 27,500 people were living with HIV/AIDS in Switzerland by March 2004.
- ❖ In the past fifteen years there had been a significant decrease in proportion of new cases among IDU (from around 40% to around 11%), and a significant increase in the proportion of heterosexually acquired HIV infections (42% for men and 79% for women in 2003). Homo and bisexual men represent a steady proportion of newly infected individuals—around 25% to 30%.
- ❖ Over one half of all heterosexually transmitted infections are among persons originating in high-prevalence countries, and around 40% among heterosexuals with partners from high-prevalence countries. Sexual partners of IDU account for only up to 17% of all heterosexually transmitted infections. 38% of all new AIDS cases reported in 2002

were foreign citizens, as well as 52% of all new HIV cases.

❖ Mandatory anonymous laboratory-based HIV case reporting started in 1987. It is supplemented with anonymous reporting from treating physicians. There are about 140 HIV screening laboratories in the countries and eleven reference centers for confirmatory HIV-testing.

Sexual Orientation

❖ In 1992 referendums in Switzerland were held. One of the results was that the age of consent for homosexuals is no longer different from that of heterosexuals.[9]

❖ In 1995, a petition was brought to the Parliament by the national gay and lesbian organization, Pink Cross, seeking partnership rights for homosexuals; the right to register one's partnership was passed in 1996.[9]

❖ There is no longer any military discrimination against homosexuals, as long as "their behavior does not disturb the discipline of military life.[10]

Prostitution[11]

❖ Prostitution is legal, and prostitutes must register with the authorities.

❖ In certain areas, street prostitution is banned.

Pornography[11]

❖ Pornography is legal, but subject to exceptions (e.g., must be 16). Hard pornography, dealing with children, animals, excrement or violence is illegal.

Resource

▶ PLANeS—Fondation Suisse pour la Santé Sexuelle et Reproductive, Av. du Beaulieu 9, P. O. Box 1229, 1001 Lausanne Switzerland.

Tel: 41 (21) 661 22 33. Website: http://www.plan-s.ch/

THAILAND

THAILAND
POPULATION: 64,631,595

CAPITAL: **BANGKOK**
POPULATION: 8,838,500

Major Cities:	Bangkok, Nakhon, Ratchasima, Chiang Mai
Ethnic Groups:	Thai 75%, Chinese 14%
Languages:	Thai (official), English
Major Religions:	Buddhist 95%; Muslim 4%
GDP per capita (PPP):	$8,300
Urban Population:	21%
Infant Mortality:	20 per 1,000 live births (1995)
Life Expectancy:	Females: 75 years; Males: 70 years
Adult Literacy:	93%
Health Care System:	1 doctor for 4,420 people; volunteer health organizations, private market government, hospitals, government health centers, traditional healers.

References
❑ *The World Almanac and Book of Facts* (2006). NY: World Almanac Education Group.
❑ *The World Factbook* http://www.cia.gov/cia/publications/factbook/ Accessed June 25, 2006.
❑ *World Reference Atlas* (2005). NY: Dorling Kindersley Publishing.

Sexual Activity

❖ Legal age of consent is 15.[1]
❖ Premarital sex is strictly forbidden.[2]
❖ Women are expected to be chaste until marriage and monogamous afterward.[2]
❖ Love affairs, premarital pregnancy, and abortions are not uncommon, but discovery is the major issue at stake.[3]
❖ Pregnancy for an unmarried woman brings shame to both her and her family.[3]
❖ Cash payments are often used to compensate the girl's parents when sexual relations outside of marriage occur.[3]
❖ Public discussion of sexual behavior is "taboo".[4]
❖ Marriage is not for love and companionship as much as it is done for economic reasons and to produce children.[4]
❖ Men have more sexual freedom than women; this is not only permitted but expected.[5]
❖ Among Thai men, polygamous relationships and frequenting prostitutes is common.[5]

Contraception

❖ The most prevalent method of birth control is female sterilization, followed by the Pill. The least popular method is the condom.[5]
❖ Oral contraceptives, injectables and IUDs are modern methods that have helped slow the population growth of Thailand.[5]
❖ Extended network ties affect contraceptive choice. The more external kinship ties households have, the more likely women in those households are to use modern forms of contraception.[6]

Abortion[5]

❖ Abortion is technically illegal except in cases of rape or threat to the woman's health.

❖ Abortion is often the chosen method in cases of premarital pregnancy; either done in an urban clinic or by traditional methods of ingesting "hot" medicine or forceful massage. These methods are extremely painful and detrimental to the woman's health.

Sex Education

❖ A National AIDS Committee was formed to help wage a nationwide AIDS education campaign with condom use as the centerpiece for the campaign.[2]
❖ School education on AIDS was initiated in 1990. At this time, the Thai HIV/AIDS research community was also extremely active in conducting quantitative and qualitative studies of risk behavior and its determinants. These studies demonstrated that the idea of individual risk that had been dominant in the beginning of the epidemic was too narrow to address the underlying social, cultural, and economic forces driving the epidemic in Thailand. Thus, the concept of individual risk was broadened to include the influence of the social environment. Conventional AIDS education evolved to foster life-skills empowerment in Thai youth rather than behavior modification, so that their culture, peer pressure, and norms would promote safer sex behavior.[7]
❖ Thailand's well-funded, politically supported and comprehensive prevention programs have reduced the annual number of HIV infections from 143,000 in 1991 to 29,000 in 2001.[8]

Sexually Transmitted Infections (including HIV)

❖ In Thailand, national adult HIV prevalence was estimated at 1.4% in 2005.[8]
❖ Prevention efforts have resulted in declining levels of HIV since the late 1990s as fewer men bought sex and condom use rates rose. However, recent

studies show that premarital sex has become more commonplace among young Thais and more than one-third of HIV infections in 2005 were among women who had been infected by their long-term partners.[9]

❖ The Thai government was slow in responding to HIV/AIDS since the disease was associated with both Westerners and gays.[5]

❖ In 1991, all government-sponsored sexually transmitted disease (STD) clinics began to promote condom use in the commercial sex setting. The "100% condom program" enlisted the cooperation of sex establishment owners and sex workers to encourage all clients to use condoms when obtaining sex. The government supplied almost 60 million free condoms a year to support this activity.[7]

❖ From 1989 to 1993, the use of condoms in commercial sex increased from 14% to 94%.[10]

❖ Sexually transmitted infections including HIV/AIDS are a grave threat to all women in Thailand as long as male partners continue to frequent brothels and other sex establishments while maintaining steady relationships.[5]

❖ Girls aged 10–14 have the highest rates or rural-urban migration; HIV infection rate in child prostitutes is now approaching 50%.[11]

Sexual Orientation

❖ There is approximately 1 million homosexuals in Thailand, one of the highest rates in the world.[4]

❖ While in general Thailand has one of the world's more liberal sexual cultures in terms of public tolerance of homosexual and transgender men and women, pockets of intense homophobia do exist.[12]

❖ On December 26, 1996 the Rajabat Institute Council, the collective governing body of all of Thailand's teachers colleges, declared that it would bar homosexuals from enrolling in any of its colleges nationwide. The announcement brought strong criticism from human rights groups and many others, who are urging the repeal of this discriminatory policy. In a [subsequent] positive development, the Commission on Justice and Human Rights of the Thai Parliament discussed the matter and decided that the ban goes against human rights principles.[12]

❖ There are no laws against homosexuality yet there are laws on consent, 15 years for relations between two people and 18 years for sex with a prostitute.[12]

Prostitution

❖ In 1960 the Prohibiting Prostitution Act was passed making prostitution, brothel keeping, and procurement illegal in Thailand.[3]

❖ In 1966 the Entertainment Places Act offered an alternative to the old style brothels: massage parlors, nightclubs, bars, coffee shops, tea houses and barber shops.[3]

❖ During the Vietnam War Thailand was the R&R center for the American troops. The sex industry was so well established that after the war ended Thailand had to attract an alternative clientele or dis-employ thousands of workers.[13]

❖ Female sexuality plays a critical role in Thailand's economic development and growth.[5] Prostitution is looked at as a means to support the family and provide for basic material needs.[3]

❖ The commercial sex industry is ruled by the cold, hard laws of economics. New money and changing tastes are bringing younger and younger girls and boys into the business. There is an estimated 100,000 children under the age of 18 working as prostitutes.[14]

❖ Thailand is the international symbol of the child prostitution problem; it is a place where children are disposable, dragged out of school as early as 6th grade, their virginity sold by their parents to brothels.[15]

❖ 75% of all men have had sex with a prostitute.[11]

Pornography[3]

❖ Although pornography is largely thought of as published materials: books, magazines, and photographs, this is not the case in Thailand where live sex shows, dances, strip and peep shows go on daily. Shows include single, duo and trio acts.

Resources

▶ Planned Parenthood Association of Thailand, 8 Soi Dai Dee, Vibhavadi-Rangsit Super Hwy, Lard-Yao, Bangkhen, Bangkok 9, Thailand. Tel: 2 5790084 or 2 5790086.

▶ Population and Community Development Association, 8 Sukhumvit Rd., SOI-12, Bangkok 10110, Thailand. Tel: 2 2560080 or 2 2558804.

TURKEY

TURKEY

POPULATION: 70,413,958

CAPITAL: **ANKARA**

POPULATION: 3,582,000

Major Cities:	Istanbul, Ankara, Izmir, Adana
Ethnic Groups:	Turk 80%, Kurd 20%
Languages:	Turkish (official), Kurdish, Dimli, Azeri, Kabardian
Major Religions:	Muslim 99.8%
GDP per capita (PPP):	$8,200
Urban Population:	74%
Infant Mortality:	40 per 1,000 live births
Life Expectancy:	Females: 75 years; Males: 70 years
Adult Literacy:	86%
Health Care System:	1 doctor per 980 people; National Health Care system, government hospitals, health centers, health houses and the private health care market.

References

❑ *The World Almanac and Book of Facts* (2006). NY: World Almanac Education Group.
❑ *The World Factbook* http://www.cia.gov/cia/publications/factbook/ Accessed June 25, 2006.
❑ *World Reference Atlas* (2005). NY: Dorling Kindersley Publishing.

Sexual Activity

❖ Age of consent for heterosexual relations is 18.[1]

❖ Illegal virginity tests are commonly conducted on unmarried women who are in police detention, or women who are applying for government jobs. These tests were also administered to "suspicious" female students in schools. The tests are no longer allowed to be given in schools (as of February 1995).[2]

❖ An intact hymen is "the most valuable piece of a girl's trousseau" for Turkish men.[3]

❖ Women who have broke the cardinal rule of purity are sent back to their parents' home where "she will carry her shame to her grave", and receive rough treatment by her unforgiving family.[3]

Contraception[4]

❖ Turkey, which has a history of progressive policies and legislation designed to improve maternal and child health, legalized family planning education and the provision of temporary contraceptive methods in the mid-1960s; legalization of abortion and sterilization followed later, in 1983.

❖ Currently, Turkey's family planning program is relatively advanced and has helped the country achieve a total contraceptive prevalence rate of 64%. There is still a high degree of reliance on traditional methods, however. Withdrawal, the most popular method, was used by 24% of currently married women in 1998.

❖ Turkish couples also strongly desire small families, and two-thirds want no more children. Yet the high failure rate of Turkey's most popular method—i.e., a pregnancy rate of 33% associated with withdrawal—combined with the widely held desire for smaller families has resulted in high levels of unintended pregnancy and of abortion.

Abortion

❖ Abortion has become more frequent since 1983, when abortion became available upon request.[5]

❖ Abortions are available on request up to 10 weeks; for over 10 weeks in cases of: risk to woman's life or risk to fetal health or handicap. A report from two specialists is needed in cases of risk to the woman or fetus health.[5]

❖ Married women need consent from their husbands and minors need consent from parents, guardian or magistrate's court.[6]

❖ The inadequacy of family planning services for abortion clients, which leads to many women to go on to have repeat abortions, constitutes a major public health issue in Turkey.[4]

❖ Women turn to abortion simply because contraceptive options are not readily available. Once quality family planning services are made available to abortion clients, they accept family planning methods at high rates.[4]

Sex Education

❖ A Sex Education Task Force was established by the Family Planning Association to convince the Ministry of National Education that sex education needs to become a priority.[7]

❖ The FPA broadcasts a weekly educational radio and TV program 'Healthy Family—Happy Society', with audience feedback. It also runs personal and telephone helpline counseling services.[8]

Sexually Transmitted Infections (including HIV)

❖ An estimated 3,700 people were living with HIV/AIDS in Turkey at the end of 2004.[9]

❖ HIV testing is mandatory for blood donors, prostitutes and military service conscripts abroad.[9]

- All diagnosed HIV-infections are reported in a national HIV case reporting system.
- Turkey has a low level epidemic and commercial sex worker can be seen as the major driver. Other vulnerable sectors include IDUs, MSM, and detainees in prison.[9]
- As in all countries in the initial stage of the epidemic, stigma and discrimination are widespread in Turkey.[9]
- High rates of syphilis are reported in both Turkish and immigrant female prostitutes in Istanbul, and high rates of syphilis are found in male prostitutes.[10]

Sexual Orientation

- Sisters of Venus, the first Turkish lesbian group was established in July 1994. It is helping to report on women's legal situation in Turkey, including a comprehensive report on lesbians' rights. They also provide educational material on AIDS for Turkish women.[11]
- Same-sex love can be found in Turkish history as far back as 1207, when the great Sufi poet Jelal al-Din Rumi, held a passion for youth.[12]
- The city of Istanbul is thought to have half a million gay people living there.[12]
- Although there are no Turkish laws that make it a crime to be a homosexual or to lead a homosexual life, gay people still conceal their homosexuality.[13]

- The Justice Commission of the Turkish Parliament accepted on July 31, 1996 a bill stating that those people who conduct "unnatural sexual intercourse" shall be expelled from the Army.[14]
- Article 10 of the Law of Associations can be used to make gay groups illegal.[14]

Prostitution

- Prostitution is illegal but tolerated in Turkey.[15]
- Women from Romania and Russia are coming to Turkey to trade sexual favors to earn money for a legitimate business back home, this is called the `Natasha Syndrome'.[15]
- There are both male and female brothels.[16]
- Some brothels are legal. Women who work there must have legal licenses and are supervised by police doctors and given clean bills of health.[16]

Pornography

- Since 1996 it is no longer a punishable offense to bring pornographic magazines to schools.[11]
- Modest editions of *Penthouse* and similar magazines are sold at newsstands, bolder ones in white cellophane covers.[15]
- Private Turkish and foreign satellite television stations now beam in X-rated programs.[15]

Resources

▶ Family Planning Association of Turkey, Türkiye Aile Planlamasi Dernegi (TAPD), Cemal Nadir Sok. No:11 Çankaya/Ankara, Turkey. Tel: 90 (312) 441 78 00 / +90 (312) 441 79 00. Website: *http://www.tapd.org.tr/*

▶ Turkish Family Health & Planning Foundation, Sitesi A Blok D.3-4, 80660 Entiler, Istanbul, Turkey.

UNITED KINGDOM

Major Cities:	In England (50 M): London 7.5 million
	In Scotland (5 M): Edinburgh 0.5 million
	In Wales (3 M): Cardiff: 0.3 million
	In N. Ireland (1.5 M): Belfast: 0.3 million
Ethnic Groups:	White 92%, Black 2%
Languages:	English, Welsh, Scottish form of Gaelic
Major Religions:	Christian (Anglican, etc) 72%, Muslim 3%
GDP per capita (PPP):	$30,300
Urban Population:	89%
Infant Mortality:	5 per 1,000 births
Life Expectancy:	Females: 81 years; Males: 76 years
Adult Literacy:	100%
Health Care System:	National health care; 1 doctor per 667 persons.

References:
❏ *The World Almanac and Book of Facts* (2006). NY: World Almanac Education Group.
❏ *The World Factbook* http://www.cia.gov/cia/publications/factbook/ Accessed June 25, 2006.
❏ *World Reference Atlas* (2005). NY: Dorling Kindersley Publishing.

Sexual Activity

❖ Age of consent is 16 for heterosexual and homosexual sex.[1]

❖ Nearly 2/3rds (64%) of young women surveyed in Great Britain said they began having sex before age 18.[2]

❖ Typical age of first intercourse: 16 years old.[3]

❖ A comparison of Western and Northern Europe and the US showed that the UK had the highest teen pregnancy rate, exceeded only by the US. The teen birth rate in the UK is twice as high as in Germany, three times as high as in France, and six times as high as in The Netherlands.[4]

❖ In response to the high rate of teen pregnancies, as well as the risk to teen parents for social exclusion, a target has been set to cut the rate of conceptions among under 18s in half by the year 2010. A report released by the government in June 1999 entitled, *Teenage Pregnancy*, outlined plans to accomplish this goal through a national campaign, better prevention, and better support services for pregnant and parenting teens.[5]

❖ Three quarters of teen pregnancies are unplanned.[5]

❖ In a study comparing teens in the UK to teens in The Netherlands about their reasons for having sexual intercourse for the first time, the teens in the UK were more likely to say it was due to peer pressure or opportunity, whereas teens in The Netherlands were much more likely to say it was due to love or commitment.[6]

Contraception

❖ Only about half of under 16s and two-thirds of 16–19s use contraception when they start to have sex.[7]

❖ Use of contraception by teens is low compared with other European countries. The reasons young people give for this include: ignorance about contraception, lack of access, and lack of confidence in discussing it with a partner.[5]

❖ Since April 1974, all contraceptive advice provided by the NHS and all prescribed supplies were made available free of charge irrespective of age or marital status.[8]

❖ Health professionals can provide contraceptive advice and treatment to those under 16 without parental consent in certain circumstances.[9]

❖ Mirena, an IUD used widely in Scandinavia, was approved for use in the UK in 1995.[10]

❖ Emergency contraception has been available since 1983; however, a major public education campaign was launched in 1995.[11]

❖ Emergency contraception is now sold over the counter.[12]

Abortion

❖ Legal up to 24 weeks, with permission of 2 physicians (however, it is still illegal in Northern Ireland).[13]

❖ Despite a national health service, more than 50% of women have to find and pay for their abortions in private clinics.[14]

❖ Girls under 16 may give written permission to an abortion without parental knowledge, if the doctor feels it is in her best interest.[2]

❖ MIFEPRISTONE/RU 486 has been available since 1991.[15]

❖ Over one-third of conceptions to under 20s end in abortion, while half of conception to under 16s end in abortion.[5]

❖ Abortion rates have remained stable since 1980 in England and Wales.[16]

Sex Education[5]

❖ In England and Wales, sex education is required in secondary schools. The basic biology—puberty, where do babies come from and so on—is part of the science national curriculum.

❖ Primary schools in England are required by law to have a policy on sex education. Secondary schools are required by law to make provision for sex education. Sex education is not fully defined by the law, but it must include education about HIV/AIDS and other STIs. Parents have a legal right to withdraw their children from sex education, except for those parts that are within the National Curriculum.

❖ In Scotland, jurisdiction over the provision of sex education lies with the local education authority. In Northern Ireland, sex education is not mandated, although it is encouraged in the teaching of health education.

Sexually Transmitted Infections (including HIV)

❖ An estimated 73,000 people were living with HIV/AIDS in the United Kingdom at the end of 2006.[17]

❖ Risk of HIV acquisition in UK is highest for gay men. Two-thirds of the UK cases are in London.[17]

❖ From 1999 onwards, there have been more diagnoses of heterosexually acquired HIV infection; 64% of HIV diagnoses heterosexually acquired were probably acquired in sub-Saharan Africa.[17]

❖ Testing is mandatory for blood donors and voluntary otherwise. All detected HIV-infected cases are reported in a national database, using an identifying code.[17]

❖ There have been increases in other STIs, especially gonorrhea, Chlamydia and genital warts.[17]

❖ Sixteen to 19 year olds have the highest rates of increase in gonorrhea of any age group, with a 45% increase in new cases in 1995–1997 alone.[5]

❖ Chlamydia affects teenage girls more than any other age group, with a 53% increase between 1995 and 1997.[5]

❖ The prevalence of genital warts among teenagers has also increased by 25% from 1995 to 1997.[5]

❖ GUM (Genito-Urinary Medicine) clinics are part of the National Health Service, offering free and confidential medical services.[5]

Sexual Orientation

❖ Despite its thriving lesbian and gay community, highly effective lobbying organizations, and several "out" government ministers and Members of Parliament, the UK has the most repressive legal situation of any country in Western Europe other than Cyprus. Discriminatory privacy, soliciting, and age of consent laws for gay men (recently equalized); a ban on lesbian and gays in the armed forces (until 2000), resulting in an average of one dismissal every week; the notorious Section 28, which bans the "promotion of homosexuality" by local authorities, introduced during the Thatcher era in 1988; and no protection in employment (indeed, case law which accepts discriminatory practices). With such a backward situation, it is hardly surprising that anti-discrimination and registered partnership laws are unimaginable for many years; and that a number of cases against the UK government are (or have recently been) before the European Court of Human Rights, including the age of consent, the armed forces, and privacy.[18]

❖ In January 2000, Britain was forced by a decision of the European Court to lift its ban on gays in the military. A new code of conduct stipulates that "inappropriate sexual behavior between personnel on duty—and not a person's sexual orientation—would be a punishable offense."[19]

Prostitution

❖ Prostitution is technically legal, but several surrounding activities are outlawed which make it hard to work legally. For example, it is illegal to solicit or advertise, run a brothel, or curb-crawl.[20]

❖ So-called tart cards are cards found in phone booths in London, Hove and Brighton that advertise the services of call girls. They are typically placed in phone booths by professional "carders", who tour the phone booths, replacing cards which have been removed by the telephone companies' cleaners. Placing them in phone booths is now illegal, although this has only reduced their number, rather than eliminating them.[21]

❖ The English Collective of Prostitutes is working to decriminalize prostitution.[22]

Pornography

❖ The major means of regulation of pornography have been through the *Customs Consolidation Act 1876* (which controls imports), the *Obscene Publications Act 1956* (publishing an obscene article for gain), and the *Indecent Displays Act 1981* (which makes it an offense to display in public material which is indecent or may cause offense or embarrassment to the public).[23]

❖ The Williams Committee of Great Britain was established in 1977 to review pornography; their conclusion that the effect of pornography was a nuisance rather than harm provided the basis for its recommendation that the principal method of controlling pornography should be to restrict its availability, primarily so that children and young adults and those who had no interest in the material would be less likely to come in contact with it.[24]

❖ Specific legislation addressing the use of children in pornography is provided by the Protection of Children Act 1978 (which makes it an offence to publish, distribute or take an indecent photo of a child) and the Criminal Justice Act 1988 (which makes it an offence to possess an indecent photo of a child).[23]

❖ Viewing Internet child pornography means committing an offence.[25]

Resources

▶ Family Planning Association of the UK, 2/12 Pentonville Road, London N1 9FP ENGLAND. Tel: 44 (20) 79 23 52 09. Website: *http://www.fpa.org.uk/*

▶ Sex Education Forum, National Children's Bureau, 8 Wakely Street, London EC1V 7QU ENGLAND. Tel: 020 7843 1901 Website: *http://www.ncb.org.uk/sef*

UNITED STATES

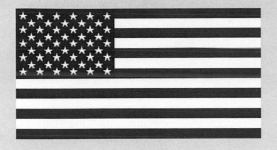

UNITED STATES
POPULATION: 298,444,215

CAPITAL: WASHINGTON, DC
POPULATION: 570,898

Major Cities:	New York, Los Angeles, Chicago, Houston, Philadelphia
Ethnic Groups:	White 82%; Black 13%, Asian 4%
Languages:	English (official) 82%, Spanish 11%
Major Religions:	Protestant 52%, Catholic 24%, Mormon 2%, Jewish 1%, Muslim 1%
GDP per capita (PPP):	$41,800
Urban Population:	76%
Infant Mortality:	6 per 1,000 births
Life Expectancy:	Females: 81 years; Males: 75 years
Adult Literacy:	99%
Health Care System:	Private physicians, publicly funded clinics; no national health insurance; 1 doctor per 435 persons.

References
❑ *The World Almanac and Book of Facts* (2006). NY: World Almanac Education Group.
❑ *The World Factbook* http://www.cia.gov/cia/publications/factbook/ Accessed June 25, 2006.
❑ *World Reference Atlas* (2005). NY: Dorling Kindersley Publishing.

Sexual Activity

* Legal age of consent for sex varies from state to state, however for most states it is 16 years of age. Some states still have laws against sex between same-sex partners (Kansas, Oklahoma, Missouri, Arkansas, and Texas), and about a dozen others have laws against oral and anal sex for anyone.[1]

* Nearly 2/3rds (63%) of young women surveyed said they began having sex before age 18.[2]

* Typical age of first intercourse: 16–17 years old; most young people begin having sex in their mid to late teens, about 8 years before they marry.[3]

* Although rates of teen births in the U.S. are at their lowest level in the 6 decades for which data exist, this rate is still higher than other industrialized countries.[4]

* Compared to other countries such as Canada, Sweden, France, and Great Britain, the U.S. has the highest rates of teen pregnancies, births, abortions, and STIs, and a higher proportion of teens report no contraceptive use at first and most recent intercourse.[5]

* Teens in the U.S. are more likely to have sexual intercourse before the age of 15 and have shorter and more sporadic relationships than teens in other countries. As a result, they are more likely to have more than one partner in a given year.[5]

* Most of the nearly 1 million U.S. teen pregnancies (78%) and teen births (66%) are unintended/not planned. In addition, nearly half of pregnancies to American women are unintended.[6]

Contraception

* Overall, the contraceptive method teen girls most frequently use is the Pill (44%), followed by the condom (38%).

Only 10% rely on the injectable, 4% withdrawal and 3% on the implant.[3]

* About three-fourths of teenage girls say they used contraception at first intercourse; most often they used a condom at first intercourse.[5]

* Of the 3 million unintended pregnancies each year in the U.S., half are to women who said they were using contraceptives—either inconsistently or incorrectly.[7]

* Since 1968, the government has provided family planning funding (Title X); the 2,500 federally funded family planning agencies operate 5,200 clinic sites, one of the most common providers is Planned Parenthood.[8]

* Parental notification is not required for teens to get birth control.[8]

* Emergency contraception sold as Plan B (also called "morning after," "aftersex" or "post-coital" birth control) can be used within 72 hours of unprotected intercourse to prevent pregnancy. It is available without prescription for women and men 18 and older. Experts estimate that easy access could reduce the number of abortions in the U.S. by half. If you are under 18, you will need a prescription to purchase emergency contraception.[9]

Abortion

* Abortion was made legal in a few states in 1970 and throughout the country in 1973 by the Supreme Court. The *Roe v Wade* decision prohibits states from restricting abortion in the first trimester (available at her request) and allows states to regulate abortion to assure its safety in the second trimester and prohibit it, except to save the pregnant women's life or health in the third trimester.[10]

* In subsequent rulings, the Court has upheld the right to abortion, while giving states the right to legislate various

kinds of restrictions. For example, state laws have been enacted that require notification of husbands or, in the case of minors, a parent; require a waiting period of up to 24 hours; and/or prohibit the use of pubic facilities for abortions.[11]

❖ The U.S. adopted the first-ever federal ban on abortion entitled the "Partial-Birth Abortion Act of 2003." The ban outlaws a range of the safest and most common abortions, performed as early as 12 weeks and fails to provide any exception if a woman's health is at stake. Enforcement of the law has been blocked by three federal courts.[12]

❖ One-third of teens say they would consider an abortion; in reality, 50% of pregnancies to unmarried teens end in abortions.[13]

❖ Although most teens (61%) who have abortions do so with at least one parent's knowledge, 32 states now have mandatory parental consent or notification laws in effect for a minor seeking an abortion.[14]

❖ Almost half of all women will have at least 1 abortion by age 45.[14]

❖ 2/3 of all abortions are among never-married women.[14]

❖ Access to abortion is a concern: 86% of all U.S. counties have no abortion provider.[14]

❖ RU-486/Mifepristone ("abortion pill') was approved for marketing in 2000 as an alternative to surgical abortion. It must be taken within 63 days of pregnancy. It causes a woman to have her period; therefore, anything attached to the wall of her uterus will be expelled as if she is menstruating.[15]

Sex Education[16]

❖ Only 19 states, including the District of Columbia, require schools to provide sexuality education. However, in many states these mandates or policies preclude teaching about such subjects as intercourse, abortion, masturbation, homosexuality, condoms and safer sex.

❖ Thirty-six states, including the District of Columbia, require schools to provide STI, HIV, and/or AIDS education. However, in some of these states require that education teach abstinence-only until marriage and not information on safer sex or condom use.

❖ The vast majority of Americans support sexuality education. In every opinion poll, more than 8 in 10 parents want sexuality education taught in high schools. Support for HIV/AIDS education is even higher.

❖ An evaluation of 23 programs found sexuality education programs do not hasten the onset of intercourse, not do they increase the frequency of intercourse or the number of sexual partners; skill-based programs can significantly delay the onset of sexual intercourse and increase contraceptive and condom use among sexually experienced youth.

❖ While the federal government does not have a policy about sexuality education and has never taken an official position on the subject, a number of federal programs have been instituted in recent years that provide funding for strict abstinence-only-until-marriage education.

❖ In 1996, the federal government created an entitlement program, Section 510(b) of Title V of the Social Security Act, that funnels $50 million per year for five years into states. Despite research showing that abstinence-only programs do not work (i.e., do not have an effect on delaying the onset of intercourse), funding for abstinence-only-until-marriage education has increased nearly 3,000% since it was created in 1996. The federal government has since approved an additional $50 million dollars of funding for abstinence-only-until-marriage.

❖ Numerous studies and evaluations published in peer-reviewed literature suggest that comprehensive sexuality education (covering a wide range of topics, including abstinence, contraception and condom use) is an effective strategy to help young people delay their involvement in sexual intercourse. Research has also concluded that these programs do not hasten the onset of sexual intercourse, do not increase the frequency of sexual intercourse, and do not increase the number of a partners sexually active teens have.

❖ Officials at the National Institutes of Health, The Institute of Medicine, the U.S. Centers for Disease Control and Prevention, the White House Office on National AIDS Policy, and the Surgeon General's Office have all publicly supported sexuality education programs that included information about abstinence, contraception, and condom use. Prominent public health organizations also support comprehensive sexuality education including the American Medical Association, the American Academy of Pediatrics, the American College of Obstetrics and Gynecology, and the Society for Adolescent Medicine. In fact, more than 127 mainstream national organizations focusing on young people and health issues including Advocates for Youth, Girls Inc., the National Association for the Advancement of Colored People, and the YWCA of the USA have joined together as the National Coalition to Support Sexuality Education committed to assuring comprehensive sexuality education for all youth in United States.

Sexually Transmitted Infections (including HIV)

❖ Out of a concern for the rising number of STIs, including HIV, as well as concern for other issues of unplanned pregnancy, abortion and sexual abuse, the Surgeon General issued a report in 2001 entitled, *Call to Action to Promote Sexual Health and Responsible Sexual Behavior*. This purpose of the report was to initiate a national dialogue on issues of sexuality, sexual health, and responsible sexual behavior.[17]

❖ STIs infect approximately 12 million persons each year.[17]

❖ The epidemic has altered demonstrably in the past decade. An estimated 40,000 people have been infected with HIV each year in the United States during the past decade, but the epidemic is now disproportionately lodged among African Americans (over 50% of new HIV diagnoses in recent years have been among African Americans) and is affecting much greater numbers of women (African American women account for up to 72% of new HIV diagnoses in all US women).[18]

❖ An estimated 1.7 million people had been infected with HIV in the United States.[19]

❖ Women account for an increasing proportion of people with HIV and AIDS, but men still account for the largest proportion.[19]

❖ Male-to-male sexual contact, still the predominant mode of HIV exposure, accounted for 41% of all recent AIDS diagnoses, and 54% of cases recently diagnosed among men.[19]

❖ Racial/ethnic disparities among people with HIV and AIDS continue to increase; 58% were non-Hispanic black or Hispanic, and 41% were White non-Hispanic black or Hispanic.[19]

❖ The proportion of AIDS cases attributed to heterosexual contact has continued to increase, and accounted for 22% of recently diagnosed cases (11% of cases among men, and 59% of cases among women).[19]

❖ Injection drug use accounted for 30% of all recently diagnosed AIDS cases (27% of cases among men, and 38% cases among women).[19]

❖ After the introduction of antiretroviral therapy in 1995–1996, AIDS-related deaths fell steeply in the United States until the late 1990s and then continued to decline more gradually. However, the rate of death due to AIDS among African Americans was over twice as high as that among whites in 2002. African Americans now have the poorest survival rates among people diagnosed with AIDS.[18]

❖ U.S. teenagers have higher STI rates than teens in other industrialized countries because they have more sexual partners and lower levels of condom use.[20]

❖ Approximately 25% of all new STIs are in teenagers.[21]

❖ Not including HIV, the most common STIs are: Chlamydia, Gonorrhea, Syphilis, Genital Herpes, Human Papilloma Virus (HPV), Hepatitis B, and Trichomoniasis.[20]

❖ Number of new cases each year:[21]

Chlamydia	3 million
Gonorrhea	650,000
Syphilis	700,000
Genital Herpes	1 million
HPV	5.5 million
Hepatitis B	120,000
Trichomoniasis	5 million

❖ Chlamydia is the most commonly reported infectious disease in the United States. It is as common as the common cold. Most people (75% of women, 50% of men) have no symptoms; therefore the majority of cases go undiagnosed.[21]

❖ The U.S. gonorrhea rate remains the highest of any industrialized country: roughly 50 times higher then Sweden and 8 times higher than Canada.[21]

❖ More than 1 in 5 Americans - or 45 million people—are currently infected with genital herpes.[21]

Sexual Orientation

❖ The United States does not have a federal law against discrimination due to sexual orientation. There are fourteen countries that have national laws that protect gays, lesbians, and bisexuals from discrimination: Canada, Denmark, Finland, France, Iceland, Ireland, Israel, The Netherlands, New Zealand, Norway, Slovenia, South Africa, Spain and Sweden.[22]

❖ California, Connecticut, Hawaii, Massachusetts, Minnesota, New Jersey, Rhode Island, Vermont and Wisconsin (the first state) have passed civil rights laws that include sexual orientation. The U. S. Supreme Court has ruled that an amendment to the Colorado State Constitution that would have banned anti-discrimination laws based on sexual orientation violated the equal protection clause of the U. S. Constitution and was, therefore, unlawful. This ruling is a landmark victory for equal rights and may provide an important precedent for future U.S. anti-discrimination cases.[22]

❖ As of 2007, California and Massachusetts recognize same-sex marriage, while Connecticut, the District of Columbia, Hawaii, Maine, New Hampshire, New Jersey, Oregon and Vermont grant persons in same-sex unions a similar legal status to those in a civil marriage by domestic partnership, civil union or reciprocal beneficiary laws. However, in many states, laws and constitutional amendments have been passed forbidding any recognition of same sex marriage. Virginia law, the most far-reaching, forbids recognition of any benefits similar to those of marriage between people of the same sex.[23]

❖ By the end of the 20th Century Sodomy laws were repealed or overturned in most American states, and those that still remained were ruled unconstitutional in the June 2003 ruling in *Lawrence v. Texas*. Many companies and local governments have clauses in their nondiscrimination policies that prohibit discrimination on the basis of sexual orientation. In some jurisdictions in the

U.S., gay bashing is considered a hate crime and given a harsher penalty.[23]

❖ Homosexuals have served in the military, some openly, since Valley Forge; yet since 1943 it has been the official policy of the U.S. military to exclude homosexuals from serving. The Defense Department contends that the purpose of excluding gays and lesbians is to preserve the order, discipline, and morale of the military, because some heterosexual soldiers would not want to serve with and take orders from homosexuals. While gays and lesbians legally serve in the armed forces of most countries around the world, the U.S. military has continued to support the view that allowing homosexuals in the armed services would be detrimental.[24]

❖ In 1993 Congress passed the National Defense Authorization Act barring gays and lesbians from openly serving in the military. The "don't ask, don't tell, don't pursue" policy of the Clinton administration permitted gays and lesbians to serve as long as they did not openly reveal their sexual orientation. A 1997 U.S. District Court ruling struck down the ban as unconstitutional.[25]

❖ In response to a Pentagon report in 2000 showing that anti-gay harassment was widespread in the military, the U.S. Department of Defense expanded the "don't ask, don't tell" policy to include "don't harass." [25]

❖ The symbolic birth of the gay rights movement occurred in 1969 in New York city when police raided a gay bar, the Stonewall. Police raids on gay bars were common occurrences, but this time the bar's patrons resisted and fought back. A riot ensued and did not end until the following day. The Stonewall incident served as a catalyst for the formation of gay rights groups, and activities such as Gay Pride Week and parades are held in yearly commemoration of the Stonewall riot.[26]

Prostitution[27]

❖ Prostitution is illegal except in certain counties of Nevada where is it restricted to state-licensed brothels. Technically the laws regarding prostitution apply both to the seller of sex (the prostitute) and the purchaser of sex (the client, the john); however, it is more often the prostitute than the customer who is charged with a crime.

❖ Over a million people have worked as prostitutes in the United States.

❖ Several organizations are working for the rights of prostitutes including COYOTE (Call Off Your Old Tired Ethics), the U.S. Prostitutes Collective, and the National Task Force on Prostitution.

Pornography

❖ Pornography, sexually explicit material meant to be sexually arousing, has been subject to many laws throughout recent history. Since 1973, individual states have been allowed to develop their own legislation.[28]

❖ Pornography is an $8 billion dollar a year business. Half of all adult videos in the U.S. are bought or rented by women alone or women in couples.[29]

❖ In 1997 the U.S. Supreme Court ruled for the first time on government regulation of the Internet. The Court struck down the Communications Decency Act, a federal law that sought to shield children from indecent material online by making the transmission of "obscene, lewd, lascivious, filthy or indecent" images, e-mail, text files, or other on-line communications punishable by up to $100,000 in fines and 2 years in prison. The Court declared the Act was too vague, and a violation of First Amendment rights. In May 2000 the Supreme Court ruled that Congress went too far when it passed the Telecommunications Act of 1996, a law meant to shield children from sexually explicit cable television programming.[30]

❖ The U.S. is the leading producer (73%) of on-line pornography.[31]

❖ Child pornography is against the law. In 1977, the U.S. passed the Protection of Children Against Sexual Exploitation Act. Since then, those involved in child pornography have been vigorously prosecuted. In 2003, the U.S. Supreme Court upheld a provision of the Children's Internet Protection Act that requires public libraries receiving federal funding to put anti-porn Internet filters on their computers or lose funding.[32]

Resources

▶ Advocates for Youth, Suite 750, 2000 M Street NW, Washington, DC 20036. Tel: 202/419-3420; Website: *http://www.advocatesforyouth.org*

▶ American Assoc. of Sex Educators, Counselors & Therapists, P.O. Box 1860, Ashland, VA. 23005. Tel: 804/752-0026; Website: *http://www.aasect.org*

▶ Planned Parenthood Federation of America, 434 West 33rd Street, New York, NY 10001. Tel: 212/541-7800; Website: *http://www.plannedparenthood.org*

▶ Sex Information and Education Council of the United States (SIECUS), 130 West 42nd Street, Suite 350, New York, NY 10036. Tel: 212/819-9770; Website: *http://www.siecus.org*

▶ Society for the Scientific Study of Sexuality (SSSS), P.O. Box 416, Allentown, PA 18105. Tel: 610/530-2483; Website: *http://www.ssc.wisc.edu/ssss/*

ZIMBABWE

ZIMBABWE

POPULATION: 12,236,805

CAPITAL: **HARARE**

POPULATION: 2,331,400

Major Cities:	Harara, Bulawayo, Chitungwiza
Ethnic Groups:	African 98% (Shona 2%, Ndebele 14%)
Languages:	English (official); Shona, Sindebele
Major Religions:	Syncretic (part Christian, part indigenous beliefs) 50%, Christian 25%, indigenous beliefs 24%
GDP per capita (PPP):	$2,300
Urban Population:	35%
Infant Mortality:	52 per 1,000 births
Life Expectancy:	Females: 38 years; Males: 40 years
Adult Literacy:	91%
Health Care System:	1 doctor per 7,100 persons; 71% of population has access to health services.

References

❑ *The World Almanac and Book of Facts* (2006). NY: World Almanac Education Group.

❑ *The World Factbook* http://www.cia.gov/cia/publications/factbook/ Accessed June 25, 2006.

❑ *World Reference Atlas* (2005). NY: Dorling Kindersley Publishing.

Sexual Activity

❖ Legal age of consent for sex is 12/16; it is illegal for same sex relations.[1]
❖ The average age of first intercourse is 18.[2]
❖ All oral and anal sex is prohibited.[3]
❖ "Multi-partnering" has become a feature of life for all men.[4]

Contraception

❖ Condom availability is very inadequate and expensive; the equivalent of five condoms per adult per year are imported.[4]
❖ The most commonly used forms of birth control are the Pill, injection, condoms and IUD.[5]
❖ Zimbabwe has one of the highest rates of modern contraception prevalence in Africa; 38%.[6]
❖ Although condom vending machines are accessible in clubs and bars, there are widespread taboos around the subject of sexuality, making it difficult for individuals to purchase the condoms.[7]
❖ Contraceptives are not readily available to women under the age of 18.[8]
❖ Early safety trials and focus-group discussions are underway in a number of countries, including Zimbabwe. Scientists have intensified their work to develop contraceptive technologies (such as vaginal microbicides) to prevent diseases such as AIDS and other STIs, especially those methods that are controlled by women. [9]

Abortion[8]

❖ Abortion is legal when:
  ◆ the woman has been raped or is a victim of incest.
  ◆ the fetus has genetic defects.
  ◆ it is to save the women's life or preserve physical health.

Sex Education

❖ The Zimbabwe National Family Planning Council has been offering programs geared at educating parents of teens on human sexuality.[10]
❖ A 1997–1998 multi-media campaign to promote sexual responsibility among young people was found to be very successful. This approach increased the reach and impact of reproductive health interventions directed to young people. Building community support for behavior change was also found to be essential, to ensure that young people find approval for their actions and have access to services.[2]

Sexually Transmitted Infections (including HIV)

❖ Zimbabwe has one of the highest AIDS prevalence rates in the world. HIV infection rates are highest before age 25, and among teenagers, women are especially vulnerable.[2]
❖ One-third of those aged 15–49 are estimated to be infected with HIV/AIDS.[11]
❖ In Zimbabwe, where 1.7 million people are living with HIV, data have shown a decline in HIV prevalence which is currently estimated at 20.1%, down from 22.1% in 2003. This decline is twofold; studies have shown both a substantial increase in condom use since the early 1990's and that more young people have been delaying their sexual début and reducing the number of casual sexual partners; however, a significant factor in the decline is attributed to high-mortality rates.[12]
❖ The government of Zimbabwe has attempted to combat HIV/AIDS through a number of locally-based programs. For example, in the eastern border town of Mutare, where an estimated 37% of pregnant women are HIV positive, programs include treatment of STIs, the

tracing of patients' contacts, an HIV peer-education program, outreach to commercial sex workers, the distribution of 150,000 condoms per month, and a home-based care program.[9]

Sexual Orientation[13]

❖ Zimbabwean law recognizes three classes of "unnatural offences": sodomy, bestiality, and a "residual group of proscribed 'unnatural' sexual acts referred to generally as 'an unnatural offence'" The absence of any definition of this third category enables any sexual act between men that falls short of sodomy to fall within it, provided there is a precedent, i.e. the act has previously been mentioned in court. These categories make no distinction between consensual and non-consensual acts, with the result that sentencing is inconsistent in lower courts, with consensual acts punished excessively, and non-consensual acts punished leniently.

❖ The most recent cases dealt with by the high courts in Zimbabwe suggest that consensual sexual behavior between adult men should no longer be punished with a custodial sentence; however, because of the tendency of magistrates' courts to punish such acts more severely, those men whose cases do not reach the high courts are likely to continue serving harsh custodial sentences.

❖ There is no record of any case where two women have been prosecuted for committing an "unnatural offence".

❖ On January 1, 2000 President Robert Mugabe attacked homosexuality in his New Year address, saying that homosexual relations were an abomination and rotten culture. "We cannot have a man marrying a man or a woman marrying a woman here. What an abomination, a rottenness of culture, real decadence of culture. Once you impose a foreign culture on us then you naturally evoke the devil in us."

Prostitution[14]

❖ Prostitution is illegal.

Pornography

❖ No information was found.

Resources

▶ Zimbabwe National Family Planning Council, P.O. Box 220, Southerton, Harare, Zimbabwe. Tel: 263/667656.

▶ United Nations Family Planning Association (UNFPA)—South Africa, Construction House, Fifth Floor, 110 Takawira St, P.O. Box 4775, Harare, Zimbabwe. Tel: 263-4-738793.

REFERENCE

AUSTRALIA

1. Legal Age of Consent. Available at: *http://www.ageofconsent.com/*. Accessed June 20, 2006.
2. Bracher M, Santow G. Premature discontinuation of contraception in Australia. *Family Planning Perspectives*. 1992;24:58–65.
3. United Nations. *Abortion Policies: A Global Review (Vol. 1)*. New York: United Nations; 1992.
4. Condom sales in schools considered. *Facts on File*. 1992;52:336.
5. UNAIDS/WHO Epidemiological Fact Sheets by Country. Available at: *http://www.who.int/hiv/pub/epidemiology/pubfacts/en/*. Accessed June 22, 2006.
6. UNAIDS Fact Sheet: Oceania. Available at: *http://www.unaids.org/en/Regions_Countries/Regions/Oceania.asp*. Accessed June 22, 2006.
7. Dynes W, ed. *Encyclopedia of Homosexuality*. New York: Guilford; 1990.
8. Australia ends a prohibition on homosexuals in military, *The New York Times*, Nov. 24, 1992.
9. International Gay and Lesbian Human Rights Commission. Australia Action Alert. Available at: *http://www.iglhrc.org/site/iglhrc/section.php?id = 1* Accessed June 22, 2006.
10. International Planned Parenthood Federation News. *Australia Overrules Gay Union Law* (June 2006). Available at: *http://www/ippf.org* Accessed June 28, 2006.
11. The World Sex Guide: Prostitution in Australia Available at: *http://www.sexatlas.com/wsg/Australia.php*. Accessed June 24, 2006.
12. Australia's Censorship System. Available at: *http://libertus.net/censor/auscensor.html* Accessed June 26, 1996.

AUSTRIA

1. Legal Age of Consent. Available at: *http://www.ageofconsent.com/*. Accessed June 20, 2006.
2. Bennett CL, Schwartz B, Marberger M. Health care in Austria: Universal access, national health insurance and private health. *JAMA*. 1993;269:2798–2804.
3. Rolston B, Eggert, A. *Abortion In the New Europe: A Comparative Handbook*. Westport, CT: Greenwood Press; 1994.
4. Traun-Vogt G, Kostenwein W. First love and heart beat in Austria. *Choices*. 1996;25:15.
5. Meredith P, Thomas L. Planned Parenthood in Europe: *A Human Rights Perspective*. Dover, NH: Croom Helm; 1986.
6. UNICEF, *A League Table of Teenage Births in Rich Countries*. Florence, Italy: UNICEF Innocenti Centre; July 2002.
7. United Nations. *Abortion Policies: A Global Review*. New York: United Nations; 1992.
8. The Alan Guttmacher Institute. *Sharing Responsibility: Women, Society, and Abortion Worldwide*. New York: The Alan Guttmacher Institute; 1999.
9. FDA approves RU 486. *Choices*. 2000;28:32.
10. UNAIDS/WHO Epidemiological Fact Sheets by Country. Available at: *http://www.who.int/hiv/pub/epidemiology/pubfacts/ en/*. Accessed June 22, 2006.

11. International Lesbian and Gay Association. World Legal Survey: Austria. Available at: *http://www.ilga.info/Information/Legal_ survey/ilga_world_legal_survey%20introduction.htm*. Accessed June 21, 2006.

12. Harris S. Military polices regarding behavior: An international survey. *Journal of Homosexuality*. 1991;21:67–74.

13. The World Sex Guide: Prostitution in Austria Available at: *http://www.sexatlas.com/wsg/Austria.php*. Accessed June 24, 2006.

14. Stary A, Kopp W. Sexually transmitted diseases. *MedGate Access Plan*. 1991;18:159–165.

15. Francoeur, R. Austria: Pornography and Erotic. *The International Encyclopedia of Sexuality*. NY: Continuum; 2001. Available at: *http://www2.hu-berlin.de/sexology/IES/austria.html* Accessed June 28, 2006.

BELGIUM

1. Legal Age of Consent. Available at: *http://www.ageofconsent.com/*. Accessed June 20, 2006.

2. The Alan Guttmacher Institute. *Sharing Responsibility: Women, Society, and Abortion Worldwide*. New York: The Alan Guttmacher Institute; 1999.

3. Donnay F. Safe Abortions in an illegal context: Perceptions from service providers in Belgium. *Studies in Family Planning*. 1993;24:150–157.

4. UNICEF, *A League Table of Teenage Births in Rich Countries*. Florence, Italy: UNICEF Innocenti Centre; July 2002.

5. FDA approves RU 486. *Choices*. 2000;28:32.

6. Cherbonnier A. Belgium: A training programme in AIDS prevention. *Planned Parenthood in Europe*. 1990;19:17.

7. Vilar D. School sex education: Still a priority in Europe, *Planned Parenthood in Europe*. 1994;23:8.

8. UNAIDS/WHO Epidemiological Fact Sheets by Country. Available at: *http://www.who.int/hiv/pub/epidemiology/pubfacts/en/*. Accessed June 22, 2006.

9. International Gay and Lesbian Human Rights Commission. Available at: *http://www.iglhrc.org/site/iglhrc/content.php?type=1&id=91*. Accessed June 21, 2006.

10. Dynes W, ed. *Encyclopedia of Homosexuality*. New York: Guilford; 1990: 124–125.

11. The World Sex Guide: Prostitution in Belgium Available at: *http://www.sexatlas.com/wsg/Belgium.php*. Accessed June 24, 2006.

BRAZIL

1. Legal Age of Consent. Available at: *http://www.ageofconsent.com/*. Accessed June 20, 2006.

2. The Alan Guttmacher Institute. *Sharing Responsibility: Women, Society, and Abortion Worldwide*. New York: The Alan Guttmacher Institute; 1999.

3. Schmittroth L. *Statistical Record of Women Worldwide*. New York: Gale Research; 1995:614.

4. Center for Reproductive Rights. Brazil: Women of the world – Laws and policies affecting their reproductive lives. Available at: *http://www.crlp.org*. Accessed June 22, 2006.

5. Center for Reproductive Rights. *Reproductive Rights 2000: Moving Forward*. Available at: *http://www.crlp.org*. Accessed June 22, 2006.

6. UNFP. *Contraceptive Requirements and Logistics Management Needs in Brazil, Technical Report No. 21*. New York: UNFP; 1995.

7. Boland R. The current status of abortion laws in Latin America: Prospects and strategies for change. *The Journal of Law, Medicine and Ethics*. 1993;21:67–71.

8. International Planned Parenthood Federation News. *Battle to Legalize Abortion Heats up in Brazil* (January 2006). Available at: *http://www/ippf.org*. Accessed June 28, 2006.

9. Ulcer drug used for abortions in Brazil. *Contemporary Sexuality*. 1993;27:6.

10. Egypto AC, Pinto MC, Bock SD. Brazilian organization develops sexual guidance programs. *SIECUS Report*. 1996;24:16–17.

11. UNAIDS/WHO Epidemiological Fact Sheets by Country. Available at: *http://www.who.int/hiv/pub/epidemiology/pubfacts/en/*. Accessed June 22, 2006.

12. International Lesbian and Gay Association. World Legal Survey: Brazil. *http://www.ilga.info/Information/Legal_survey/ilga_world_legal_survey%20introduction.htm*. Accessed June 21, 2006.

13. Otchet A. Should prostitution be legal? UNESCO Courier. 1998;51:37–39.

14. Sachs A. The last commodity: Child prostitution in the developing world. *World Watch*. 1994;7:24–30.

15. Francoeur, R. Brazil: Pornography and Erotic. *The International Encyclopedia of Sexuality*. NY: Continuum; 2001. Available at: *http://www2.hu-berlin.de/sexology/IES/brazil.html#8*

BULGARIA

1. Goranov M, Backardjiev G. Teenage pregnancy in Bulgaria, *Planned Parenthood in Europe*. 1993;22:16.

2. Legal Age of Consent. Available at: *http://www.ageofconsent.com/*. Accessed June 20, 2006.

3. Chernev T, Hadjiev C, Stamenkova R. The cost of family planning and abortion in Bulgaria. *Planned Parenthood in Europe*. 1994;23:12–13.

4. Cherneve T, Ivanov S, Dikov I, Stamenkova R. Prospective study of contraception with Levonorgestrel. *Planned Parenthood in Europe*. 1995;24:25.

5. Carlson E, Omori M. Fertility regulation in a declining state socialist economy: Bulgaria, 1976–1995. *International Family Planning Perspectives*. 1998;24:184–187.

6. The Alan Guttmacher Institute. *Sharing Responsibility: Women, Society, and Abortion Worldwide*. New York: The Alan Guttmacher Institute; 1999.

7. UNAIDS/WHO Epidemiological Fact Sheets by Country. Available at: *http://www.who.int/hiv/pub/epidemiology/pubfacts/en/*. Accessed June 22, 2006.

8. International Lesbian and Gay Association. World Legal Survey: Bulgaria. Available at: *http://www.ilga.info/Information/Legal_survey/ilga_world_legal_survey%20introduction.htm*. Accessed June 21, 2006.

9. The World Sex Guide: Prostitution in Bulgaria Available at: *http://www.sexatlas.com/wsg/Bulgaria.php*. Accessed June 24, 2006.

10. Pornography: Bulgaria. Available at: *http://en.wikipedia.org/wiki/Pornography*. Accessed June 28, 2006.

CANADA

1. Legal Age of Consent. Available at: *http://www.ageofconsent.com/*. Accessed June 20, 2006.
2. Hanvey L. *Facts on Teenage Pregnancy*. Planned Parenthood of Canada. August 1993.
3. Mills D. *Canadian Teenagers Say They Can Wait*. Ortho-McNeil Inc., November 1992.
4. Rodman H, Trost J. *The Adolescent Dilemma*. New York: Praeger; 1986:27.
5. International Planned Parenthood Federation News. *Canada Approves Emergency Contraceptive as Non-prescription Drug* (April 2005). Available at: *http://www/ippf.org* Accessed June 28, 2008.
6. Sachdev P. *Sex, Abortion and Unmarried Women*. Westport, CT: Greenwood. 1993:1, 31.
7. United Nations. *Abortion Policies: A Global Review*. New York: United Nations; 1992:73.
8. Planned Parenthood Federation of Canada. InfoSexNet Bulletin April 2000. Available at: *http://www.ppfc.ca/issues/april2000.htm*. Accessed June 27, 2008.
9. Planned Parenthood Federation of Canada. Hot Issues: Emergency Contraceptive Pills vs. RU 486. Available at: *http://www.ppfc.ca/issues/emergency.html#4*. Accessed June 27, 2008.
10. Bennett J. Hard facts for children. *MacLean's*. Jan 12, 1987;100:38.
11. Kerr D. Condom vending machines in Canada's secondary schools. *Journal of School Health*. 1990;60:114–115.
12. UNAIDS/WHO Epidemiological Fact Sheets by Country. Available at: *http://www.who.int/hiv/pub/epidemiology/pubfacts/en/*. Accessed June 22, 2008.
13. International Gay and Lesbian Human Rights campaign. Antidiscrimination Legislation (April 1999). Available at: *http://www.iglhrc.org/site/iglhrc/section.php?id = 1*. Accessed June 22, 2008.
14. Fisher L. Armed and gay. *MacLean's*. May 24, 1993;106:14.
15. International Lesbian ad Gay Association. Spain and Canada open marriage to same-sex couples (June 30, 2005). *http://www.ilga.org/search_results.asp*. Accessed June 22, 2008.
16. O'Neill T, DeWitt P. Grandma in a short skirt. Newsmagazine (Alberta Edition). August 28, 2000:27.
17. Lewin T. Canada says pornography harms women and can be barred, *The New York Times*. Feb. 28, 1992;141:B7.
18. *Facts on File*. March 12, 1992;52:176.
19. Petiti, J. *Rights of the Child: Child pornography on the Internet*. United Nations Economic and Social Council, December 24, 2004.

CHILE

1. Legal Age of Consent. Available at: *http://www.ageofconsent.com/*. Accessed June 20, 2006.
2. Hearld J, Valenzuela M, Morris L. Premarital sexual activity and contraceptive use in Santiago, Chile. *Studies in Family Planning*. 1992;23:128–136.
3. Center for Reproductive Rights. *Women's Reproductive Rights in Chile: A Shadow Report*. Available at: *http://www.crlp.org*. June 20, 2006.
4. United Nations. *Abortion Policies: A Global Review*. New York: United Nations; 1992:82–83.
5. UNAIDS/WHO Epidemiological Fact Sheets by Country. Available at: *http://www.who.int/hiv/pub/epidemiology/pubfacts/en/*. Accessed June 22, 2006.

6. International Lesbian and Gay Association. World Legal Survey: Chile. Available at: *http://www.ilga.info/Information/Legal_survey/ilga_world_legal_survey%20introduction.htm*. Accessed June 21, 2006.

7. The World Sex Guide: Prostitution in Chile. Available at: *http://www.sexatlas.com/wsg/Chile.php*. Accessed June 24, 2006.

8. UNFPA Global Population Policy Update: Chile. Available at: *http://www.unfpa.org/parliamentarians/news/newsletters/issue23.htm*. Accessed June 27, 2006.

CHINA

1. Legal Age of Consent. Available at: *http://www.ageofconsent.com/*. Accessed June 20, 2006.

2. Zhou X. Virginity and premarital sex in contemporary China, *Feminist Studies*. 1989;15:279–288.

3. Kelly G. *Sexuality Today 8th edition*. New York, NY: McGraw-Hill; 2006: 169.

4. Jaivin L. Sex attitudes in China for the '90s. *The Wall Street Journal*. Jan, 10, 1991:A12.

5. Faison S. In China, rapid social changes bring a surge in the divorce rate. *The New York Times*. August 22, 1995:A1.

6. China's sexual revolution, *Contemporary Sexuality*. 1993;25:2–3.

7. United Nations. *Abortion Policies: A Global Review*. New York: United Nations; 1992:84–86.

8. Center for Reproductive Rights. China. Available at: *http://www.crlp.org*. Accessed June 26, 2006.

9. FDA approves RU 486. *Choices*. 2000;28:32.

10. Schmittroth L. *Statistical Record of Women Worldwide*. New York: Gale Research. 1995:614.

11. Chinese eugenics law to limit disabled births. *Contemporary Sexuality*. 1995;29:9.

12. China bans sex-screening of fetuses. *Contemporary Sexuality*. 1994;28:14.

13. UNAIDS/WHO Epidemiological Fact Sheets by Country. Available at: *http://www.who.int/hiv/pub/epidemiology/pubfacts/en/*. Accessed June 22, 2006.

14. UNAIDS Fact Sheet: Asia. Available at. *http://www.unaids.org/en/Regions_Countries/Regions/Asia.asp*. Accessed June 22, 2006.

15. Xiaobing Y. China launches anti-prostitution campaign. *Beijing Review*. Dec. 16, 1991;34:27–29.

16. Remez L. STD rates soar in China: Three in four new cases are among the unmarried. *International Family Planning Perspectives*. 2000; 26: 141–142.

17. International Lesbian and Gay Association. World Legal Survey: China. Available at: *http://www.ilga.info/Information/Legal_survey/ilga_world_legal_survey%20introduction.htm*. Accessed June 21, 2006.

18. Gang C. China declares war on pornography. *Beijing Review*. March 19, 1990;33:26–29.

19. Lili C. Discard the dross, make literature and art prosper. *Beijing Review*. Oct. 17, 1989;32:7.

20. NPC enacts laws on drugs, pornography. *Beijing Review*. Jan. 14, 1991;34:7.

COSTA RICA

1. Legal Age of Consent. Available at: *http://www.ageofconsent.com/*. Accessed June 20, 2006.

2. McCauley AP, Salter C. Growing numbers, diverse needs. *Population Reports*. 1995;23:3–11.

3. The Alan Guttmacher Institute. Teenage Sex Occurs Mostly Outside Marriage For Men and Within Marriage For Women Around The World. Available at: *http://www.alanguttmacher.org/*. Accessed October 26, 2002.

4. Smith-Morris M. *The Economist Book of World Vital Statistics*. New York: Times Books; 1990.

5. IPPF Country Profiles: Costa Rica. Available at: *http://ippfnet.ippf.org/pub/IPPF_Regions/ IPPF_CountryProfile.asp?ISOCode = CR*. Accessed June 26, 2006.

6. Pan American Health Organization. *Emergency Contraception in the Americas*. Available at: *http://www.paho.org*. Accessed June 27, 2006.

7. Carroll JL, Wolpe PR. *Sexuality and Gender in Society*. New York: Harper Collins Publishers; 1996:452.

8. Victory against hedonistic sex "education" in Costa Rica. Available at: *http://www.vidahumana.org/english/ hispanics/hispanics-costarica.html*. Accessed June 27, 2006.

9. UNAIDS/WHO Epidemiological Fact Sheets by Country. Available at: *http://www.who.int/ hiv/pub/epidemiology/pubfacts/en/*. Accessed June 22, 2006.

10. International Lesbian and Gay Association. World Legal Survey: Costa Rica. *http://www.ilga.info/Information/ Legal_survey/ilga_world_legal_survey% 20introduction.htm*. Accessed June 21, 2006.

11. The World Sex Guide: Prostitution in Costa Rica Available at: *http://www. sexatlas.com/ wsg/ Costa-Rica.php*. Accessed June 24, 2006.

CUBA

1. Legal Age of Consent. Available at: *http://www.ageofconsent.com/*. Accessed June 20, 2006.

2. United Nations. *Abortion Policies: A Global Review*. New York: United Nations; 1992.

3. Cuban hookers rounded up at infamous resort. *Knight-Rider Newspaper*. June 7, 1996.

4. UNAIDS/WHO Epidemiological Fact Sheets by Country. Available at: *http://www.who.int/ hiv/pub/epidemiology/pubfacts/en/*. Accessed June 22, 2006.

5. UNAIDS/WHO Fact Sheet: Caribbean. Available at: *http://www.unaids.org/en/ Regions_Countries/Regions/Caribbean.asp*. Accessed June 22, 2006.

6. Dynes W, ed. *Encyclopedia of Homosexuality*. New York: Guilford; 1990:285–87.

7. International Lesbian and Gay Association. World Legal Survey: Cuba. *http://www.ilga. info/Information/Legal_survey/ilga_world_ legal_survey%20introduction.htm*. Accessed June 21, 2006.

8. Prostitution soars as tourists return to Cuba. *Contemporary Sexuality*. 1995;29:8.

CZECH REPUBLIC

1. Legal Age of Consent. Available at: *http://www.ageofconsent.com/*. Accessed June 20, 2006.

2. Kastanlova V. Increasing sexually transmitted disease rates among prostitutes in the Czech Republic. *Journal of Community Health*. 1995;20:219–223.

3. Uzel R, Wynnyczuk V. Private fee no barrier to family planning in the Czech Republic. *Planned Parenthood in Europe*. 1994;23:10–11.

4. Visser A, Uzel R, Ketting E, Bruyniks N, Oddens B. Practice, attitudes and knowledge of Czech and Slovak gynaecologists concerning contraception. *Planned Parenthood in Europe*. 1994;23:19–23.

5. Camp S. A study-tour report on emergency contraception in seven European countries. Washington, DC: Reproductive Health Technologies Project; 1994.

6. United Nations. *Abortion Policies: A Global Review*. New York: United Nations; 1992.

7. Vilar D. School sex education: Still a priority in Europe. *Planned Parenthood in Europe*. 1994;23:8–12.

8. UNAIDS/WHO Epidemiological Fact Sheets by Country. Available at: *http://www.who.int/hiv/pub/epidemiology/pubfacts/en/*. Accessed June 22, 2006.

9. International Lesbian and Gay Association. World Legal Survey: Czech Republic. *http://www.ilga.info/Information/Legal_survey/ilga_world_legal_survey%20introduction.htm*. Accessed June 21, 2006.

10. Carty C. Media Change in the Czech Republic. Available at: *http://www.utexas.edu/ftp/pub/eems/czech-republic.html*. Accessed June 27, 2006.

11. Czech Penthouse launched. *CTK National News Wire*, April 12, 1994.

DENMARK

1. Legal Age of Consent. Available at: *http://www.ageofconsent.com/*. Accessed June 20, 2006.

2. *Sexual Rights of Young Women*. Denmark: The Danish Family Planning Association and The Swedish Association for Sex Education; 1995.

3. The Alan Guttmacher Institute. *Sharing Responsibility: Women, Society, and Abortion Worldwide*. New York: The Alan Guttmacher Institute; 1999.

4. Christensen A. Restoring sexual hangovers with few side effects. *Planned Parenthood in Europe*. 1995;24:18.

5. United Nations. *Abortion Policies: A Global Review*. New York: United Nations; 1992:106.

6. Rahman A, Katzive L. A global review of laws on induced abortion, 1985–1997. *International Family Planning Perspectives*. 1998;24:56–64.

7. Henshaw SK, Singh S, Haas T. Recent trends in abortion rates worldwide. *International Family Planning Perspectives*. 1999;25:44–48.

8. FDA approves RU 486. *Choices*. 2000;28:32.

9. UNAIDS/WHO Epidemiological Fact Sheets by Country. Available at: *http://www.who.int/hiv/pub/epidemiology/pubfacts/en/*. Accessed June 22, 2006.

10. International Gay and Lesbian Human Rights campaign. Antidiscrimination Legislation (April 1999). Available at: *http://www.iglhrc.org/site/iglhrc/section.php?id=1* Accessed June 21, 2006.

11. International Lesbian and Gay Association. World Legal Survey: Denmark. *http://www.ilga.info/Information/Legal_survey/ilga_world_legal_survey%20introduction.htm*. Accessed June 21, 2006.

12. Kimmel M. *Men confront pornography*. New York: Crown Publishers;1990:233, 244.

EGYPT

1. Legal Age of Consent. Available at: *http://www.ageofconsent.com/*. Accessed June 20, 2006.

2. Miller N. *Out in the World: Gay and Lesbian Life from Buenos Aries to Bangkok*. New York: Random House; 1992:78–90.

3. Crosette B. In Cairo, please to stop maiming girls: Foes show models of mutilated female genitals. *The New York Times*. Sept. 11, 1994:6.
4. Berhane R. The facts about FGM in Egypt: An overview. *WIN News*. 1994;20:30.
5. Center for Reproductive Rights. *Implementing Adolescent Reproductive Rights Through the Convention on the Rights of the Child*. Available at: *http://www.crlp.org*. Accessed June 22, 2006.
6. Trottier D, Potter L, Taylor B, Glover L. Reports: User characteristics and oral contraceptive compliance in Egypt. *Studies in Family Planning*. 1994;25:284–292.
7. Egypt 1992: Results from the Demographic and Health Survey. *Studies in Family Planning*. 1994;25:243–247.
8. UNICEF, *A League Table of Teenage Births in Rich Countries*. Florence, Italy: UNICEF Innocenti Centre; July 2002.
9. United Nations. *Abortion Policies: A Global Review*. New York: United Nations; 1992:118.
10. Huntington D, Hassan E, Attallah N, Toubia N, Naguib M, Nawar L. Improving the medical care counseling of post abortion patients in Egypt. *Studies in Family Planning*. 1995;26:351.
11. FDA approves MIFEPRISTONE/RU 486. *Choices*. 2000;28:32.
12. International Planned Parenthood Federation News. Religious Figures in Egypt Argue over Virtue of Sex Education (April 2005). Available at: *http://www.ippf.org* Accessed June 28, 2006.
13. UNAIDS/WHO Epidemiological Fact Sheets by Country. Available at: *http://www.who.int/hiv/pub/epidemiology/pubfacts/en/*. Accessed June 22, 2006.
14. International Lesbian and Gay Association. World Legal Survey: Egypt. *http://www.ilga.info/Information/Legal_survey/ilga_world_legal_survey%20introduction.htm*. Accessed June 21, 2006.
15. The World Sex Guide: Prostitution in Egypt. Available at: *http://www.sexatlas.com/wsg/Egypt.php*. Accessed June 24, 2006.
16. Jehl D. Egyptians say Israel is waging a sex war. *The New York Times*. Oct 10, 1995:A5.

FINLAND

1. Legal Age of Consent. Available at: *http://www.ageofconsent.com/*. Accessed June 20, 2006.
2. The Alan Guttmacher Institute. *Sharing Responsibility: Women, Society, and Abortion Worldwide*. New York: The Alan Guttmacher Institute; 1999.
3. Kosunen M, Rimpela M. Improving adolescent sexual health in Finland. *Choices*. 1996;25:18.
4. Lähteenmäki P, Suhonen S, Elnoma K. Use of post-coital contraception in Finland is increasing. *Planned Parenthood in Europe*. 1995;24:13–14.
5. Rolston B, Eggert, A. *Abortion In the New Europe: A Comparative Handbook*. Westport, CT: Greenwood Press; 1994:88.
6. *Abortion Laws in Europe*. National Abortion Campaign. London, England;1995.
7. Henshaw SK, Singh S, Haas T. Recent trends in abortion rates worldwide. *International Family Planning Perspectives*. 1999;25:44–48.
8. FDA approves RU 486. *Choices*. 2000;28:32.
9. UNAIDS/WHO Epidemiological Fact Sheets by Country. Available at: *http://www.who.int/hiv/pub/epidemiology/pubfacts/en/*. Accessed June 22, 2006.
10. Lottes IL. Sexual health policies in other industrialized countries: Are there lessons for the United States? *Journal of Sex Research*. 2002;39:79–83.
11. International Gay and Lesbian Human Rights campaign. Antidiscrimination

Legislation (April 1999). Available at: *http://www.iglhrc.org/site/iglhrc/section.php? id = 1* Accessed June 22, 2006.

12. International Lesbian and Gay Association. World Legal Survey: Finland. *http://www.ilga.info/Information/Legal_ survey/ilga_world_legal_survey%20 introduction.htm.* Accessed June 21, 2006.

13. The World Sex Guide: Prostitution in Finland. Available at: *http://www.sexatlas.com/ wsg/Finland.php.* Accessed June 24, 2006.

14. Pornography: Finland. Available at: *http://en.wikipedia.org/wiki/Pornography.* Accessed June 28, 2006.

FRANCE

1. Legal Age of Consent. Available at: *http://www.ageofconsent.com/.* Accessed June 20, 2006.

2. ACSsF Investigator. AIDS and sexual behavior in France. *Nature.* 1992;360:397–407.

3. The Alan Guttmacher Institute. *Sharing Responsibility: Women, Society, and Abortion Worldwide.* New York: The Alan Guttmacher Institute; 1999.

4. France cuts condom prices. *The New York Times.* Dec. 5, 1993:14.

5. UNICEF, *A League Table of Teenage Births in Rich Countries.* Florence, Italy: UNICEF Innocenti Centre; July 2002.

6. Rolston B, Eggert A. *Abortion In the New Europe: A Comparative Handbook.* Westport, CT: Greenwood Press; 1994.

7. Center for Reproductive Rights. France extends abortion law. Available at: *http://www.reproductiverights.org/ww_ europe.html.* Accessed June 28, 2006.

8. Rahman A, Katzive L. A global review of laws on induced abortion, 1985–1997. *International Family Planning Perspectives.* 1998;24:56–64.

9. FDA approves RU 486. *Choices.* 2000;28:32.

10. Jones RK, Henshaw SK. Mifepristone for early medical abortion: Experiences in France, Great Britain and Sweden. *Perspectives on Sexual and Reproductive Health.* 2002;34:154–161.

11. Vilar D. School sex education: Still a priority in Europe. *Planned Parenthood in Europe.* 1994;23:8–12.

12. UNAIDS/WHO Epidemiological Fact Sheets by Country. Available at: *http://www.who.int/ hiv/ pub/epidemiology/pubfacts/en/.* Accessed June 22, 2006.

13. Facts of File, *Weekly World News Digest.* February 12, 1996.

14. International Gay and Lesbian Human Rights campaign. Antidiscrimination Legislation (April 1999). *http://www.iglhrc.org/site/ iglhrc/section.php?id = 1* Accessed June 22, 2006.

15. International Gay and Lesbian Human Rights Commission. Available at: *http://www.iglhrc.org/site/iglhrc/content.php? type = 1&id = 91.* Accessed June 21, 2006.

16. International Lesbian and Gay Association. World Legal Survey: France. *http://www.ilga. info/Information/Legal_survey/ilga_world_ legal_survey%20introduction.htm.* Accessed June 21, 2006.

17. The World Sex Guide: Prostitution in France. Available at: *http://www.sexatlas.com/wsg/ France.php.* Accessed June 24, 2006.

18. Pornography: France. Available at: *http://en.wikipedia.org/wiki/Pornography.* Accessed June 28, 2006.

GERMANY

1. Legal Age of Consent. Available at: http://www.ageofconsent.com/. Accessed June 20, 2006.
2. The Alan Guttmacher Institute. *Sharing Responsibility: Women, Society, and Abortion Worldwide*. New York: The Alan Guttmacher Institute; 1999.
3. Aresin L. East Germany two years after unification. *Planned Parenthood in Europe*.1993;22:11–12.
4. Ellertson C. Expanding access to emergency contraception in developing countries. *Family Planning Perspectives*. 1995;26:251–263.
5. Center for Reproductive Rights. The World's Abortion Laws: Recent Changes and Recommendations for Action. Available at: http://www.crlp.org/. Accessed June 22, 2006.
6. Rahman A, Katzive L. A global review of laws on induced abortion, 1985–1997. *International Family Planning Perspectives*. 1998;24:56–64.
7. Von Baross J. German constitutional court rejects abortion compromise. *Planned Parenthood in Europe*. 1993;22:14–16.
8. FDA approves RU 486. *Choices*. 2000;28:32.
9. Von Baross J. The 'yo-yo effect' of public family planning funding in Germany. *Planned Parenthood in Europe*. 1994;23:5–7.
10. Center for Reproductive Rights. Women of the World – Germany. Available at http://www.crlp.org/pub_bo_wowlaw_ger.html. Accessed June 22, 2006.
11. UNAIDS/WHO Epidemiological Fact Sheets by Country. Available at: http://www.who.int/hiv/pub/epidemiology/pubfacts/en/. Accessed June 22, 2006.
12. Dynes W, ed. *Encyclopedia of Homosexuality*. New York: Guilford; 1990.
13. International Lesbian and Gay Association. World Legal Survey: Germany. http://www.ilga.info/ Information/Legal_survey/ilga_world_legal_survey%20introduction.htm. Accessed June 21, 2006.
14. The World Sex Guide: Prostitution in Germany. Available at: http://www.sexatlas.com/wsg/Germany.php. Accessed June 24, 2006.
15. Prostitution: Germany. Available at: http://en.wikipedia.org/wiko/Prostitution. Accessed June 27, 2006.
16. Francoeur, R. Germany: Pornography and Erotic. *The International Encyclopedia of Sexuality*. NY: Continuum; 2001. Available at: http://www2.hu-berlin.de/sexology/IES/Germany.html
17. Pornography: Germany. Available at: http://en.wikipedia.org/wiki/Pornography. Accessed June 28, 2006.

GREECE

1. Legal Age of Consent. Available at: http://www.ageofconsent.com/. Accessed June 20, 2006.
2. Snyder P. *The European Women's Almanac*. New York: Columbia Univ. Press; 1992:152.
3. United Nations. *Abortion Policies: A Global Review*. New York: United Nations; 1992:31–33.
4. Tseperi P, Mestheneos E. Paradoxes in the costs of family planning in Greece. *Planned Parenthood in Europe*. 1994;23:14.
5. UNICEF, *A League Table of Teenage Births in Rich Countries*. Florence, Italy: UNICEF Innocenti Centre; July 2002.
6. Naziri D. The trivality of abortion in Greece. *Planned Parenthood in Europe*. 1991;20:12.
7. FDA approves RU 486. *Choices*. 2000;28:32.
8. Vilar D. School sex education: Still a priority in Europe. *Planned Parenthood in Europe*. 1994;23:8–12.

9. Mestheneos L. PPA Profile: Greece. *Planned Parenthood in Europe*. 1992;21:36–37.
10. UNAIDS/WHO Epidemiological Fact Sheets by Country. Available at: *http://www.who.int/hiv/pub/epidemiology/pubfacts/en/*. Accessed June 22, 2006.
11. International Lesbian and Gay Association. World Legal Survey: Greece. Available at: *http://www.ilga.info/Information/Legal_survey/ilga_world_legal_survey%20introduction.htm*. Accessed June 21, 2006.
12. Harris S. Military policies regarding homosexual behavior: An international survey. *Journal of Homosexuality*. 1991; 21:67–74.
13. Otchet A. Should prostitution be legal? UNESCO Courier. 1998;51:37–39.
14. Richlin A. *Pornography and Representation in Greece and Rome*. New York: Oxford University Press;1994:54.
15. Kelly G. *Sexuality Today* 8th ed. New York: McGraw-Hill Publishing: 2006:447.

HUNGARY

1. Legal Age of Consent. Available at: *http://www.ageofconsent.com/*. Accessed June 20, 2006.
2. Camp S. "Postinor: The unique method of emergency contraception developed in Hungary. *Planned Parenthood in Europe*. 1995;24:23–24.
3. *Abortion Laws in Europe*. National Abortion Campaign. London, England;1995.
4. Pongracz M. Induced abortion in Hungary today: Results of a public opinion poll. *Planned Parenthood in Europe*. 1991;20:8.
5. Vilar D. School sex education: Still a priority in Europe. *Planned Parenthood in Europe*. 1994;23:8–12.
6. UNAIDS/WHO Epidemiological Fact Sheets by Country. Available at: *http://www.who.int/hiv/pub/epidemiology/pubfacts/en/*. Accessed June 22, 2006.
7. International Gay and Lesbian Human Rights campaign. Antidiscrimination Legislation (April 1999). Available at: *http://www.iglhrc.org/site/iglhrc/section.php?id=1* Accessed June 22, 2006.
8. International Lesbian and Gay Association. World Legal Survey: Hungary. *http://www.ilga.info/Information/Legal_survey/ilga_world_legal_survey%20introduction.htm*. Accessed June 21, 2006.
9. The World Sex Guide: Prostitution in Hungary. Available at: *http://www.sexatlas.com/wsg/Hungary.php*. Accessed June 24, 2006.

INDIA

1. Legal Age of Consent. Available at: *http://www.ageofconsent.com/*. Accessed June 20, 2006.
2. Sharma V, Sharma A. The letterbox approach: A model for sex education in an orthodox society. *Journal of Family Welfare*. 1995;41:31.
3. Visaria L, Jejeebhoy S, Merrick T. From family planning to reproductive health: Challenges facing India. *International Family Planning Perspectives*. 1999;25:44–49.
4. Center for Reproductive Rights. India. Available at: *http://www.crlp.org/pub_bo_wowlaw_india.html*. Accessed June 22, 2006.
5. Studies in Short: Indian researchers test reversible male sterilization. *Contemporary Sexuality*. 1995;29:4.
6. International Planned Parenthood Federation News. *Over-the-counter sale of emergency contraceptives welcomed* (September 2005). Available at: *http://www/ippf.org*. Accessed June 28, 2006.

7. Center for Reproductive Rights. *Reproductive Rights 2000: Moving Forward*. Available at: *http://www/ippf.org*. Accessed June 28, 2006.

8. International Planned Parenthood Federation News. *India Has World's Maximum Unsafe Abortions* (October 2004). Available at: *http://www/ippf.org*. Accessed June 28, 2006.

9. United Nations. *Abortion Policies: A Global Review*. New York: United Nations; 1992:57.

10. Sexuality and the law: Indian parliament bans mention of fetus's gender. *Contemporary Sexuality*. 1994;28:13,15.

11. Center for Reproductive Rights. *Promote access to the full range of abortion technologies: Removing barriers to medical abortion*. Available at: *http://www/ippf.org* Accessed June 28, 2006.

12. UNAIDS/WHO Epidemiological Fact Sheets by Country. Available at: *http://www.who.int/hiv/ pub/epidemiology/pubfacts/en/*. Accessed June 22, 2006.

13. UNAIDS Fact Sheet: Asia. Available at: *http://www.unaids.org/en/Regions_Countries/Regions/Asia.asp*. Accessed June 22, 2006.

14. Anderson JW. AIDS nears epidemic rate in India: Prostitution, blood supply, drug use blamed for spread of disease. *The Washington Post*. September 14, 1992;A1.

15. International Lesbian and Gay Association. World Legal Survey: India. *http://www.ilga.info/Information/Legal_survey/ilga_world_legal_survey%20introduction.htm*. Accessed June 21, 2006.

16. International update: Nepali girls enslaved in Bombay brothels. *Contemporary Sexuality*. 1995;29:9.

17. Sachs A. The last commodity: Child prostitution in the developing world. *World Watch*. 1994;7:24–30.

18. Aziz C. A life of hell for the wife of a god. *The Guardian*. June 10, 1995:25.

19. Kennedy J. Crime bill cracks down on child exploitation. *Christian Science Monitor*. Sept 6, 1994:19.

20. Pornography: India. Available at: *http://en.wikipedia.org/wiki/Pornography*. Accessed June 28, 2006.

IRAN

1. Legal Age of Consent. Available at: *http://www.ageofconsent.com/*. Accessed June 20, 2006.

2. Metz HC. *Iran: A country study*. Federal Research Division, Library of Congress; 1987:111.

3. Carrington T. Iran enacts family size rule. *The Wall Street Journal*, May 17, 1993:A13.

4. International Planned Parenthood Federation News. *16-Year old Iranian Woman Hanged 'For Acts Incompatible With Chastity'* (September 2004). Available at: *http://www/ippf.org*. Accessed June 28, 2006.

5. United Nations. *Abortion Policies: A Global Review*. New York: United Nations; 1992:63–64.

6. International update: Iran expands birth control options. *Contemporary sexuality*. 1996;30:9.

7. UNAIDS/WHO Epidemiological Fact Sheets by Country. Available at: *http://www.who.int/hiv/pub/epidemiology/pubfacts/en/*. Accessed June 22, 2006.

8. MacKay J. Global sex: Sexuality and sexual practices around the world. *Sexual and Relationship Therapy*. 20001:16:71–82.

9. International Lesbian and Gay Association. World Legal Survey: Iran. *http://www.ilga.info/Information/Legal_survey/ilga_world_legal_survey%20 introduction.htm*. Accessed June 21, 2006.

10. Sepehrrad R. Eighty lashes in Iran. *The Washington Post*. May 25, 1994:A22.

11. Iranian approves death penalty for makers of video pornography. *The New York Times*. December 21, 1993:5.

IRELAND

1. Legal Age of Consent. Available at: *http://www.ageofconsent.com/*. Accessed June 20, 2006.
2. FPA profile: Irish Family Planning Association. *Planned Parenthood in Europe.* 1994;23:35.
3. International Planned Parenthood Federation. Country Profile: Ireland. Available at: *http://www.ippf.org*. Obtained October 18, 2002.
4. Breakwell CM, Fife-Schaw CR. Sexual activities and preferences in a United Kingdom sample of 16–20 year olds. *Archives of Sexual Behavior.* 1992;21:271–293.
5. Rolston B, Eggert A. *Abortion In the New Europe: A Comparative Handbook.* Westport, CT: Greenwood Press; 1994:159–169.
6. United Nations. *Abortion Policies: A Global Review.* New York: United Nations; 1992:68–70.
7. International update: Irish court asked to rule on right to information on abortion. *Contemporary Sexuality.* 1995:29:11.
8. Center for Reproductive Rights. "*Women on Waves*" helping to turn the tide on abortion restrictions. Available at: *http://www.crlp. org*. Accessed June 26, 2006.
9. Vilar D. School sex education: Still a priority in Europe. *Planned Parenthood in Europe.* 1994;23:8–12.
10. UNAIDS/WHO Epidemiological Fact Sheets by Country. Available at: *http://www.who. int/hiv/pub/epidemiology/pubfacts/en/*. Accessed June 22, 2006.
11. International Gay and Lesbian Human Rights campaign. Antidiscrimination Legislation (April 1999). Available at: *http://www.iglhrc.org/site/iglhrc/section.php? id = 1*. Accessed on June 22, 2006.
12. International Lesbian and Gay Association. World Legal Survey: Ireland. *http://www.ilga. info/Information/Legal_survey/ilga_world_ legal_survey%20introduction.htm*. Accessed June 21, 2006.
13. The World Sex Guide: Prostitution in Ireland. Available at: *http://www.sexatlas.com/ wsg/Ireland.php*. Accessed June 24, 2006.

ISRAEL

1. Legal Age of Consent. Available at: *http://www.ageofconsent.com/*. Accessed June 20, 2006.
2. International Planned Parenthood Federation. Country Profile: Israel. Available at: *http://www.ippf.org*. Obtained October 18, 2002.
3. International Planned Parenthood Federation News. *Emergency Contraception Available Without Prescription in Israel* (March 2002). Available at: *http://www/ippf.org*. Accessed June 28, 2006.
4. United Nations. *Abortion Policies: A Global Review.* New York: United Nations; 1992:71–73.
5. The Alan Guttmacher Institute. *Sharing Responsibility: Women, Society, and Abortion Worldwide.* New York: The Alan Guttmacher Institute; 1999.
6. FDA approves RU 486. *Choices.* 2000;28:32.

7. Cavaglion G. The institutionalization of knowledge in Israeli sex education programs: A historical review, 1948-1987. *Journal of Sex Education and Therapy.* 2002;25:286–293.

8. UNAIDS/WHO Epidemiological Fact Sheets by Country. Available at: *http://www.who.int/hiv/pub/epidemiology/pubfacts/en/.* Accessed June 22, 2006.

9. International Gay and Lesbian Human Rights campaign. Antidiscrimination Legislation (April 1999). *http://www.iglhrc.org/site/iglhrc/section.php?id=1.* Accessed June 22, 2006.

10. International Lesbian and Gay Association. World Legal Survey: Israel. *http://www.ilga.info/Information/Legal_survey/ilga_world_legal_survey%20 introduction.htm.* Accessed June 21, 2006.

11. Riding A. In NATO, only U.S. & British ban gay soldiers. *The New York Times.* Nov. 13, 1992:A12.

12. The World Sex Guide: Prostitution in Israel. Available at: *http://www.sexatlas.com/wsg/Israel.php.* Accessed June 24, 2006.

13. Dworkin A. Israel: Whose country is it anyway? *Ms. Magazine.* Sept./Oct. 1990:68.

ITALY

1. Legal Age of Consent. Available at: *http://www.ageofconsent.com/.* Accessed June 20, 2006.

2. National Institute of Health. Attitudes of parents of high school students about AIDS, drugs, and sex education in schools: Rome, Italy. *JAMA.* 1992;267:2160–2162.

3. Perez MD, Livi-Bacci M. Fertility in Italy and Spain: The lowest in the world. *Family Planning Perspectives.* 1992;24:162–171.

4. Spinelli A, Grandolfo ME. Induced abortion and contraception in Italy. *Planned Parenthood in Europe.* 1991;20:18–19.

5. *Abortion laws in Europe.* National Abortion Campaign. London, England; 1995.

6. United Nations. *Abortion Policies: A Global Review.* New York: United Nations; 1992:74–76.

7. Henshaw SK, Singh S, Haas T. Recent trends in abortion rates worldwide. *International Family Planning Perspectives.* 1999;25:44–48.

8. Vilar D. School sex education: Still a priority in Europe. *Planned Parenthood in Europe.* 1994;23:8–12.

9. International update: AIDS gang defiant. *Contemporary Sexuality.* 1995;29:7.

10. International Planned Parenthood Federation. Country Profile: Italy. Available at: *http://www.ippf.org.* Obtained June 26, 2006.

11. UNAIDS/WHO Epidemiological Fact Sheets by Country. Available at: *http://www.who.int/hiv/pub/epidemiology/pubfacts/en/.* Accessed June 22, 2006.

12. Suligoi B, Giuliani, M Binkin N. The national STD surveillance system in Italy: Results of the first year of activity. *International Journal of STD & AIDS.* 1994;5:93–100.

13. Roure C. Overview of epidemiology and disease burden of Hepatitis B in the European region. *Vaccine.* 1995;13:18–21.

14. International Lesbian and Gay Association. World Legal Survey: Italy *http://www.ilga.info/Information/Legal_survey/ilga_world_legal_survey%20 introduction.htm.* Accessed June 21, 2006.

15. Riding A. In NATO, only U.S. & British ban gay soldiers. *The New York Times.* Nov. 13, 1992:A12.

16. Italy's supercharged street-walkers. The Economist. 1998;348:40.

JAPAN

1. Legal Age of Consent. Available at: *http://www.ageofconsent.com/*. Accessed June 20, 2006.

2. International Planned Parenthood Federation News. *Japan Alarmed by Increase in Teenage Sex* (June 2005). Available at: *http://www/ippf.org*. Accessed June 28, 2006.

3. Kelly G. *Sexuality Today 8th edition.* New York: McGraw-Hill Publishers; 2006:11.

4. International Planned Parenthood Federation. Country Profile: Japan. Available at: *http://www.ippf.org*. Accessed June 26, 2006.

5. United Nations. *Abortion Policies: A Global Review.* New York: United Nations; 1992:79–81.

6. International update: Japanese practice mourning ritual for abortions. *Contemporary Sexuality.*1996;30:4.

7. Henshaw SK, Singh S, Haas T. Recent trends in abortion rates worldwide. *International Family Planning Perspectives.* 1999;25:44–48.

8. Kitazawa K. Sexuality issues in Japan. *SIECUS Report.*1994;22:7–11.

9. UNAIDS/WHO Epidemiological Fact Sheets by Country. Available at: *http://www.who.int/hiv/pub/epidemiology/pubfacts/en/*. Accessed June 22, 2006.

10. UNAIDS Fact Sheet: High Income Countries. Available at: *http://www.unaids.org/barcelona/presskit/factsheets/Fshighincome_en..htm*. Accessed October 18, 2002.

11. International Lesbian and Gay Association. World Legal Survey: Japan. *http://www.ilga.info/Information/Legal_survey/ilga_world_legal_survey%20introduction.htm*. Accessed June 21, 2006.

12. The World Sex Guide: Prostitution in Japan. Available at: *http://www.sexatlas.com/wsg/Japan.php*. Accessed June 24, 2006.

13. Editorial: Governments crack down on the Internet. *Information Society Trends Issues.* December 2, 1996.

14. Kristof ND. In Japan, brutal comics for women. *The New York Times.* Nov. 5, 1995: E1.

15. MacKay J. Global sex: Sexuality and sexual practices around the world. *Sexual and Relationship Therapy.* 20001:16:71–82.

KENYA

1. Legal Age of Consent. Available at: *http://www.ageofconsent.com/*. Accessed June 20, 2006.

2. Barker G, Rich S. Influences on adolescent sexuality in Nigeria and Kenya: Findings from recent focus-group discussions. *Studies in Family Planning.* 1992;23:199–210.

3. Lorch D. Unsafe abortions become a big problem in Kenya. *The New York Times.* June 4, 1995;3(N).

4. Center for Reproductive Rights. Kenya. Available at: *http://www.crlp.org*. Accessed June 21, 2006.

5. Lorch D. After years of ignoring AIDS epidemic, Kenya has begun facing up to it. *The New York Times.* December 18, 1993:5.

6. Baker J, Khasiani S. Induced abortion in Kenya: Case histories. *Studies in Family Planning.* 1991;23:34–44.

7. UNAIDS/WHO Epidemiological Fact Sheets by Country. Available at: *http://www.who.int/hiv/pub/epidemiology/pubfacts/en/*. Accessed June 22, 2006.

8. International Lesbian and Gay Association. World Legal Survey: Kenya. *http://www.ilga.info/Information/Legal_survey/ilga_world_*

legal_survey%20introduction.htm. Accessed June 21, 2006.

9. Okie S. An AIDS clue in Kenya? *The Washington Post*. December 14, 1993:WH9.

10. Francoeur, R. Kenya: Pornography and Erotic. *The International Encyclopedia of Sexuality*. NY: Continuum; 2001. Available at: *http://www2.hu-berlin.de/sexology/IES/kenya.html*

MEXICO

1. Legal Age of Consent. Available at: *http://www.ageofconsent.com/*. Accessed June 20, 2006.

2. McCauley AP, Salter C. Meeting the needs of young people. *Population Reports*. 1995;41:3–11.

3. Center for Reproductive Rights. *Reproductive Rights 2000: Moving Forward*. Available at: *http://www.crlp.org*. Accessed June 26, 2006.

4. Center for Reproductive Rights. *Women's Reproductive Rights in Mexico: A Shadow Report*. Available at: *http://www.crlp.org*. Accessed June 28, 2006.

5. United Nations. *Abortion Policies: A Global Review*. New York: United Nations; 1992:142–143.

6. Kellogg EH. *The world's laws and practices on population and sexuality education*. Medford, MA: Tufts University. 1975.

7. Kelly G. *Sexuality Today, 8th edition*. New York: McGraw-Hill Publishers; 2006:169.

8. UNAIDS/WHO Epidemiological Fact Sheets by Country. Available at: *http://www.who.int/hiv/pub/epidemiology/pubfacts/en/*. Accessed June 22, 2006.

9. International Lesbian and Gay Association. World Legal Survey: Mexico. *http://www.ilga.info/Information/Legal_survey/ilga_world_legal_survey%20introduction.htm*. Accessed June 21, 2006.

10. The World Sex Guide: Prostitution in Mexico. Available at: *http://www.sexatlas.com/wsg/Mexico.php*. Accessed June 24, 2006.

NETHERLANDS

1. Legal Age of Consent. Available at: *http://www.ageofconsent.com/*. Accessed June 20, 2006.

2. Braeken D, Rademakers J, Reinders J. *Welcome to the Netherlands: A journey through Dutch approach to young people and sexual health*. Youth Incentives, Utrecht, The Netherlands. 2002.

3. Doppenberg H. Free pill in The Netherlands: For how much longer? *Planned Parenthood in Europe*. 1994;23:8–9.

4. UNICEF, *A League Table of Teenage Births in Rich Countries*. Florence, Italy: UNICEF Innocenti Centre; July 2002.

5. Ketting E. Is the Dutch abortion rate really that low? *Planned Parenthood in Europe*, 1994;23:29–32.

6. Rolston B, Eggert, A. *Abortion In the New Europe: A Comparative Handbook*. Westport, CT: Greenwood Press; 1994.

7. FDA approves RU 486. *Choices*. 2000;28:32.

8. UNAIDS/WHO Epidemiological Fact Sheets by Country. Available at: *http://www.who.int/hiv/pub/epidemiology/pubfacts/en/*. Accessed June 22, 2006.

9. International Gay and Lesbian Human Rights campaign. Antidiscrimination Legislation (April 1999). *http://www.iglhrc.org/site/iglhrc/section.php?id=1*. Accessed June 22, 2006.

10. Lambda Legal. International Recognition of Same-Sex Partnerships (March 30, 2001). *http://www.lambdalegal.org/cgi-bin/iowa/documents/records?/record = 432* Accessed June 21, 2006.

11. International Lesbian and Gay Association. World Legal Survey: The Netherlands. *http://www.ilga.info/Information/Legal_survey/ilga_world_legal_survey%20 introduction.htm.* Accessed June 21, 2006.

12. Janssen R. Gays in Dutch army. *Europe.* 1993;325:37.

13. The rule of common sense. *The Economist.* 2002;363:12–14.

14. Pornography: Netherlands. Available at: *http://en.wikipedia.org/wiki/Pornography.* Accessed June 28, 2006.

NEW ZEALAND

1. Legal Age of Consent. Available at: *http://www.ageofconsent.com/.* Accessed June 20, 2006.

2. United Nations. *Abortion Policies: A Global Review.* New York: United Nations; 1992.

3. McCauley AP, Salter C. Growing numbers, diverse needs. *Population Reports.* 1995;41: 3–11.

4. New Zealand gives way birth control to combat abortion. *Catholic World News.* May 2, 1996.

5. Jamison E. *World Population Profile.* U.S. Bureau of Census, Washington, D.C. 1994:A–42.

6. Center for Reproductive Rights. *Emergency Contraception: Contraception, Not Abortion.* Available at: *http://www.crlp.org/pub_art_icpdec2.html.* Accessed June 22, 2006.

7. Jones RK, Henshaw SK. Mifepristone for early medical abortion: Experiences in France, Great Britain and Sweden. *Perspectives on Sexual and Reproductive Health.* 2002;34:154–161.

8. International Planned Parenthood Federation. Country Profile: New Zealand. Available at: *http://www.ippf.org.* Accessed June 27, 2006.

9. Rosser BR. Male homosexual behavior and the effects of AIDS education: A study of behavior and safer sex in New Zealand and Southern Australia. New York: Praeger; 1991.

10. UNAIDS/WHO Epidemiological Fact Sheets by Country. Available at: *http://www.who.int/hiv/pub/epidemiology/pubfacts/en/.* Accessed June 22, 2006.

11. New Zealand bans discrimination. *The Dominion of Wellington, NZ.* July 29, 1993.

12. International Gay and Lesbian Human Rights campaign. Antidiscrimination Legislation (April 1999). *http://www.iglhrc.org/site/iglhrc/section.php?id = 1.* Accessed June 22, 2006.

13. International Lesbian and Gay Association. World Legal Survey: New Zealand. *http://www.ilga.info/Information/Legal_survey/ilga_world_legal_survey%20 introduction.htm.* Accessed June 21, 2006.

14. International Planned Parenthood Federation News. *New Zealand Recognizes Same-Sex Unions* (December 2004). Available at: *http://www/ippf.org.* Accessed June 28, 2006.

15. Prostitution: New Zealand. Available at: *http://en.wikipedia.org/wiki/Prostitution.* Accessed June 28, 2006.

16. Petiti, J. *Rights of the Child: Child pornography on the Internet.* United Nations Economic and Social Council, December 24, 2004.

NORWAY

1. Legal Age of Consent. Available at: *http://www.ageofconsent.com/*. Accessed June 20, 2006.
2. The Alan Guttmacher Institute. *Sharing Responsibility: Women, Society, and Abortion Worldwide*. New York: The Alan Guttmacher Institute; 1999.
3. Mahler K. Condom use increase in Norway appears related more to contraception than to disease prevention. *Family Planning Perspectives*. 1996.
4. International Planned Parenthood Federation. Country Profile: Norway. Available at: *http://www.ippf.org*. Accessed June 27, 2006.
5. UNICEF, *A League Table of Teenage Births in Rich Countries*. Florence, Italy: UNICEF Innocenti Centre; July 2002.
6. Sachdev P, ed. *International Handbook on Abortion*. New York: Greenwood Press; 1988.
7. FDA approves RU 486. *Choices*. 2000;28:32.
8. UNAIDS/WHO Epidemiological Fact Sheets by Country. Available at: *http://www.who.int/hiv/pub/epidemiology/pubfacts/en/*. Accessed June 22, 2006.
9. International Gay and Lesbian Human Rights campaign. Antidiscrimination Legislation (April 1999). *http://www.iglhrc.org/site/iglhrc/section.php?id = 1*. Accessed June 22, 2006.
10. International Lesbian and Gay Association. World Legal Survey: Norway. *http://www.ilga.info/Information/Legal_survey/ilga_world_legal_survey%20introduction.htm*. Accessed June 21, 2006.
11. Snyder P. *The European Women's Almanac*. New York, NY: Columbia University Press; 1992:262.
12. Skilbrei M. The rise and fall of the Norwegian massage parlours: Change sin the Norwegian prostitution setting in the 19s. *Feminist Review*. 2002;67:63–77.
13. Pornography: Norway. Available at: *http://en.wikipedia.org/wiki/Pornography*. Accessed June 28, 2006.
14. Petiti, J. *Rights of the Child: Child pornography on the Internet*. United Nations Economic and Social Council, December 24, 2004.

POLAND

1. Legal Age of Consent. Available at: *http://www.ageofconsent.com/*. Accessed June 20, 2006.
2. The Alan Guttmacher Institute. *Sharing Responsibility: Women, Society, and Abortion Worldwide*. New York: The Alan Guttmacher Institute; 1999.
3. Rolston B, Eggert, A. *Abortion In the New Europe: A Comparative Handbook*. Westport, CT: Greenwood Press; 1994.
4. Center for Reproductive Rights. *Reproductive Rights 2000: Moving Forward*. Available at: *http://www.crlp.org*. Accessed June 26, 2006.
5. Henshaw SK, Singh S, Haas T. Recent trends in abortion rates worldwide. *International Family Planning Perspectives*. 1999;25:44–48.
6. International Planned Parenthood Federation News. *High Levels of Illegal Abortion Found in Poland* (November 2005). Available at: *http://www/ippf.org*. Accessed June 28, 2006.
7. Mrugala G. Polish family planning in crisis: The Roman Catholic influence. *Planned Parenthood in Europe*. 1991;20:5.
8. UNAIDS/WHO Epidemiological Fact Sheets by Country. Available at: *http://www.who.int/hiv/pub/*

epidemiology/pubfacts/en/. Accessed June 22, 2006.

9. International Lesbian and Gay Association. World Legal Survey: Poland. Available at: http://www.ilga.info/Information/Legal_survey/ilga_world_legal_survey%20introduction.htm. Accessed June 21, 2006.

10. The World Sex Guide: Prostitution in Poland. Available at: http://www.sexatlas.com/wsg/Poland.php. Accessed June 24, 2006.

11. E. Zielinska E, Plakwicz J. Strengthening human rights for women and men in matters relating to sexual behaviors and reproduction. Journal of Women's History. 1994;5:91.

PORTUGAL

1. Legal Age of Consent. Available at: http://www.ageofconsent.com/. Accessed June 20, 2006.

2. The Alan Guttmacher Institute. Sharing Responsibility: Women, Society, and Abortion Worldwide. New York: The Alan Guttmacher Institute; 1999.

3. Rolston B, Eggert, A. Abortion In the New Europe: A Comparative Handbook. Westport, CT: Greenwood Press; 1994:215–227.

4. UNICEF, A League Table of Teenage Births in Rich Countries. Florence, Italy: UNICEF Innocenti Centre; July 2002.

5. Center for Reproductive Rights. Reproductive Rights 2000: Moving Forward. Available at: http://www.crlp.org. Accessed June 26, 2006.

6. Meredith P, Thomas L. Planned Parenthood in Europe: A Human Rights Perspective. London: International Planned Parenthood; 1986.

7. Vilar D. The referendum on abortion in Portugal. Choices. 1999;27:16–18.

8. UNAIDS/WHO Epidemiological Fact Sheets by Country. Available at: http://www.who.int/hiv/pub/epidemiology/pubfacts/en/. Accessed June 22, 2006.

9. UNAIDS Fact Sheet: North America, Western and Central Europe. Available at: http://www.unaids.org/en/Regions_Countries/Regions/NthAmer_West_Cent_Europe.asp. Accessed June 22, 2006.

10. Snyder P. The European Woman's Almanac. New York, NY: Columbia University Press; 1992:291.

11. International Lesbian and Gay Association. World Legal Survey: Portugal. http://www.ilga.info/Information/Legal_survey/ilga_world_legal_survey%20introduction.htm. Accessed June 21, 2006.

12. The World Sex Guide: Prostitution in Portugal. Available at: http://www.sexatlas.com/wsg/Portugal.php. Accessed June 24, 2006.

ROMANIA

1. Legal Age of Consent. Available at: http://www.ageofconsent.com/. Accessed June 20, 2006.

2. Johnson B, Horga M, Andronache L. Contraception and abortion in Romania. The Lancet. 1993;341:875-878.

3. The Alan Guttmacher Institute. Sharing Responsibility: Women, Society, and Abortion Worldwide. New York: The Alan Guttmacher Institute; 1999.

4. Serbanescu F, Morris L, Stanescu A. The impact of recent policy changes on fertility, abortion, and contraception use in Romania. Studies in Family Planning. 1995;26:81.

5. UNAIDS/WHO Epidemiological Fact Sheets by Country. Available at: *http://www.who.int/hiv/pub/epidemiology/pubfacts/en/*. Accessed June 22, 2006.
6. International Lesbian and Gay Association. World Legal Survey: Romania. *http://www.ilga.info/Information/*

Legal_survey/ilga_world_legal_survey%20 introduction.htm. Accessed June 21, 2006.
7. The World Sex Guide: Prostitution in Romania. Available at: *http://www.sexatlas.com/wsg/Romania.php*. Accessed June 24, 2006.

RUSSIAN FEDERATION

1. Legal Age of Consent. Available at: *http://www.ageofconsent.com/*. Accessed June 20, 2006.
2. Bodravo V. Russian attitudes on sex and youth. *Choices*. 1996;25:9–14.
3. Alesina I. Adolescent sexual health initiative in Russia. *Choices*. 1996;25:16–17.
4. Visser A, Remennick L, Bruyniks N. Contraception in Russia: Attitude, knowledge and practice of doctors. *Planned Parenthood in Europe*. 1993;22:26–29.
5. Mahler K. Rates of modern method use are high among urban Russian women who typically want small families. *Family Planning Perspectives*. 1998;30:293–294.
6. Ellertson C. Expanding access to emergency contraception in developing countries. *Family Planning Perspectives*. 1995;26:251–263.
7. Popov A. A short history of abortion and population policy in Russia. *Planned Parenthood in Europe*. 1993;22:23–25.
8. Center for Reproductive Rights. *Abortion and the Law: Ten Years of Reform*. Available at: *http://www.crlp.org/wn_abortion.html*. Accessed June 22, 2006.
9. The Alan Guttmacher Institute. *Sharing Responsibility: Women, Society, and*

Abortion Worldwide. New York: The Alan Guttmacher Institute; 1999.
10. FDA approves RU 486. *Choices*. 2000;28:32.
11. Zhuravleva IV. The health behavior of adolescents and sexually transmitted disease. *Russian Education & Society*. 2001;43:72–92.
12. UNAIDS/WHO Epidemiological Fact Sheets by Country. Available at: *http://www.who.int/hiv/pub/epidemiology/pubfacts/en/*. Accessed June 22, 2006.
13. International Lesbian and Gay Association. World Legal Survey: Russia. *http://www.ilga.info/Information/Legal_survey/ilga_world_legal_survey%20 introduction.htm*. Accessed June 21 2006.
14. International update: Gay Russians remain in. *Contemporary Sexuality*. 1995;29:9.
15. Anthony L. Sex and the Soviet man. *National Review*. July 8, 1988:24–25.
16. Quigley J. The dilemma of prostitution law reform. *American Criminal Law Review*. 1992;29:1192–1234.
17. Goscilo H. New members and organs: Politics of porn. *Genders*. 1995;22:164.
18. Holman R. Moscow restricts pornography. *The Wall Street Journal*. June 6, 1994:A9.

SINGAPORE

1. Legal Age of Consent. Available at: *http://www.ageofconsent.com/*. Accessed June 20, 2006.

2. David JM. Don't count on me, Singapore. *National Review*. May 16, 1994.
3. Chua J. Un-studly. *The New Republic*. January 27, 1992:11–12.

4. International Planned Parenthood Federation. Country Profile: Singapore. Available at: *http://www.ippf.org.* Accessed June 26, 2006.
5. Chaun K. *Changing contraceptive choices of Singapore women.* Available at: *http://www.singstat.gov.sg.* Accessed June 22, 2006.
6. Sachdev P, ed. *International Handbook on Abortion.* New York: Greenwood Press;1988:402–412.
7. International Planned Parenthood Federation. IPPF News: *Singapore to launch sex education programmes next year* (November 2000). Available at:

http://ippfnet.ippf.org/. Accessed June 28, 2006.
8. UNAIDS/WHO Epidemiological Fact Sheets by Country. Available at: *http://www.who.int/ hiv/pub/epidemiology/pubfacts/en/.* Accessed June 22, 2006.
9. International Lesbian and Gay Association. World Legal Survey: Singapore. *http://www.ilga.info/Information/ Legal_survey/ilga_world_legal_survey% 20introduction.htm.* Accessed June 21, 2006.
10. The World Sex Guide: Prostitution in Singapore. Available at: *http://www. sexatlas.com/wsg/Singapore.php.* Accessed June 24, 2006.

SLOVAKIA

1. Legal Age of Consent. Available at: *http://www.ageofconsent.com/.* Accessed June 20, 2006.
2. Visser A, Uzel R, Ketting E, Bruyniks N, Oddens B. Practice, attitudes and knowledge of Czech and Slovak gynaecologists concerning contraception. *Planned Parenthood in Europe.* 1994;23:19–23.
3. Chudikova A. Reproductive health challenges in the Slovak Republic. *Planned Parenthood in Europe.* 1993;22:27.
4. Camp S. Postinor: The unique method of emergency contraception developed in Hungary. *Planned Parenthood in Europe.* 1995;24:23–24.
5. *Abortion laws in Europe.* National Abortion Campaign. London, England; 1995.

6. Vilar D. School sex education: Still a priority in Europe. *Planned Parenthood in Europe.* 1994;23:8–12.
7. UNAIDS/WHO Epidemiological Fact Sheets by Country. Available at: *http://www.who. int/ hiv/pub/epidemiology/pubfacts/en/.* Accessed June 22, 2006.
8. International Lesbian and Gay Association. World Legal Survey: Slovakia. *http://www. ilga.info/Information/Legal_survey/ilga_ world_legal_survey%20introduction.htm.* Accessed June 21, 2006.
9. The World Sex Guide: Prostitution in Slovakia. Available at: *http://www. sexatlas.com/wsg/Slovakia.php.* Accessed June 24, 2006.

SOUTH AFRICA

1. Legal Age of Consent. Available at: *http://www.ageofconsent.com/.* Accessed June 20, 2006.
2. Lucas D. Fertility and family planning in southern and central Africa. *Studies in Family Planning.* 1992:23:31–39.

3. Apartheid gone, anything goes. *The New York Times.* December 28, 1994:A7.
4. Dan O. Population studies in South Africa. *Studies in Family Planning.* 1993;24:
5. Ellertson C. Expanding access to emergency contraception in developing countries.

Family Planning Perspectives. 1995;26:251–263.

6. Center for Reproductive Rights. *Reproductive Rights 2000: Moving Forward.* Available at: *http://www.crlp.org.* Accessed June 26, 2006.

7. The Alan Guttmacher Institute. *Sharing Responsibility: Women, Society, and Abortion Worldwide.* New York: The Alan Guttmacher Institute; 1999.

8. FDA approves RU 486. *Choices.* 2000;28:32.

9. UNAIDS/WHO Fact Sheet: Sub-Saharan Africa. Available at: *http://www.unaids.org /en/Regions_Countries/Regions/SubSaharan Africa.asp.* Accessed June 22, 2006.

10. UNAIDS Epidemiological Fact Sheets by Country. Available at: *http://www.who.int/ hiv/pub/epidemiology/pubfacts/en/.* Accessed June 22, 2006.

11. International Gay and Lesbian Human Rights campaign. Antidiscrimination Legislation (April 1999). *http://www.iglhrc.org/site/iglhrc/ section.php?id = 1.* Accessed June 22, 2006.

12. International Lesbian and Gay Association. World Legal Survey: South Africa. *http://www.ilga.info/Information/ Legal_survey/ilga_world_legal_survey% 20introduction.htm.* Accessed June 21, 2006.

13. The World Sex Guide: Prostitution in South Africa. Available at: *http://www.sexatlas.com/ wsg/South-Africa.php.* Accessed June 24, 2006.

14. Wells K. The new South Africa sheds Calvinist past and mutates daily. *The Wall Street Journal.* June 9, 1995:A1.

15. Petiti, J. *Rights of the Child: Child pornography on the Internet.* United Nations Economic and Social Council, December 24, 2004.

SPAIN

1. Legal Age of Consent. Available at: *http://www.ageofconsent.com/.* Accessed June 20, 2006.

2. Nieto E, DeCiria L. FPA youth programme in Spain. *Choices.*1996;25:5–7.

3. Perez M, Livi-Bacci M. Fertility in Italy and Spain: The lowest in the world. *Family Planning Perspectives.* 1992;24:162–171.

4. Perez R. Emergency contraception at a youth service centre. *Planned Parenthood in Europe.* 1995;24:11–12.

5. *Abortion laws in Europe.* National Abortion Campaign. London, England; 1995.

6. Fuster I. Spain about to change its abortion law. *Planned Parenthood in Europe.* 1994;23:27–28.

7. Gasco M. Spain still in need of a good abortion law. *Planned Parenthood in Europe.* 1991:20:15–17.

8. FDA approves RU 486. *Choices.* 2000;28:32.

9. UNAIDS/WHO Epidemiological Fact Sheets by Country. Available at: *http://www.who.int/ hiv/pub/epidemiology/pubfacts/en/.* Accessed June 22, 2006.

10. UNAIDS Fact Sheet: High Income Countries. Available at: *http://www.unaids.org/ barcelona/presskit/factsheets/Fshighincome_ en..htm.* Accessed June 24, 2006.

11. International Gay and Lesbian Human Rights campaign. Antidiscrimination Legislation (April 1999). *http://www.iglhrc. org/site/iglhrc/section.php?id = 1.* Accessed June 22, 2006.

12. International Lesbian and Gay Association. World Legal Survey: Spain. *http://www.ilga.info/Information/ Legal_survey/ilga_world_legal_survey%20 introduction.htm.* Accessed June 21, 2006.

13. International Lesbian ad Gay Association. Spain and Canada open marriage to same-sex couples (June 30, 2006). *http://www.ilga.org/search_results.asp.* Accessed June 22, 2006.

14. The World Sex Guide: Prostitution in Spain. Available at: *http://www.sexatlas.com/wsg/ Spain.php.* Accessed June 24, 2006.

SWEDEN

1. Legal Age of Consent. Available at: *http://www.ageofconsent.com/*. Accessed June 20, 2006.

2. The Danish Family Planning Association and Swedish Association for Sex Education. *The Sexual Rights of Young Women in Denmark and Sweden.* (Denmark: Clausen Offset; 1995.

3. Lewin B, ed. *Sex in Sweden: On the Swedish Sexual Life.* Stockholm, Sweden: The National Institute of Public Health; 2000.

4. Snyder P. *European Women's Almanac.* New York: Columbia Univ. Press: 1992;330–332.

5. Rogala C, Anzen B. Late start for emergency contraception in Sweden. *Planned Parenthood in Europe.* 1995;24:15–17.

6. Persson E, Gustafsson B, van Rooijen M. Subsidizing contraception for young people in Sweden. *Planned Parenthood in Europe.* 1994;23:2–4.

7. Ellertson C. Expanding access to emergency contraception in developing countries. *Family Planning Perspectives.* 1995;26:251–263.

8. Henshaw SK, Singh S, Haas T. Recent trends in abortion rates worldwide. *International Family Planning Perspectives.* 1999;25:44–48.

9. FDA approves RU 486. *Choices.* 2000;28:32.

10. Jones RK, Henshaw SK. Mifepristone for early medical abortion: Experiences in France, Great Britain and Sweden. *Perspectives on Sexual and Reproductive Health.* 2002;34:154–161.

11. Bygdeman M, Lindahl K. *Sex Education and Reproductive Health in Sweden in the 21st Century.* Stockholm, Sweden: Swedish Government Official Report; 1994:49.

12. Vilar D. School sex education. Still a priority in Europe. *Planned Parenthood in Europe.* 1994;23:8–12.

13. Lottes IL. Sexual health policies in other industrialized countries: Are there lessons for the United States? *Journal of Sex Research.* 2002;39:79–83.

14. UNAIDS/WHO Epidemiological Fact Sheets by Country. Available at: *http://www.who.int/hiv/pub/epidemiology/pubfacts/en/*. Accessed June 22, 2006.

15. Harris S. Military policies regarding homosexual behavior: An international survey. *Journal of Homosexuality.* 1991;21:67–74.

16. International Lesbian and Gay Association. World Legal Survey: Sweden. *http://www.ilga.info/Information/Legal_survey/ilga_world_legal_survey%20introduction.htm* Accessed June 21, 2006.

17. Prostitution: Sweden. Available at: *http://en.wikipedia.org/wiki/Prostitution.* Accessed June 28, 2006.

18. Petiti, J. *Rights of the Child: Child pornography on the Internet.* United Nations Economic and Social Council, December 24, 2004.

SWITZERLAND

1. Legal Age of Consent. Available at: *http://www.ageofconsent.com/*. Accessed June 20, 2006.

2. The Alan Guttmacher Institute. *Sharing Responsibility: Women, Society, and Abortion Worldwide.* New York: The Alan Guttmacher Institute; 1999.

3. Narring F, Michaud PA, Vinit S. Demographic and behavioral factors associated with adolescent pregnancy in Switzerland. *Family Planning Perspectives.* 1996;28:232–236.

4. Rolston B, Eggert, A. *Abortion In the New Europe: A Comparative Handbook.* Westport, CT: Greenwood Press; 1994:262–263.

5. Center for Reproductive Rights. *Abortion and the Law: Ten Years of Reform.* Available at: *http://www.crlp.org/wn_abortion.html.* Accessed June 22, 2006.

6. FDA approves RU 486. *Choices.* 2000;28:32.

7. AIDS and women: A Swiss perspective. *Feminist Review.* 1992;41:58–63.
8. UNAIDS/WHO Epidemiological Fact Sheets by Country. Available at: *http://www.who.int/ hiv/pub/epidemiology/pubfacts/en/*. Accessed June 22, 2006.
9. International Lesbian and Gay Association. World Legal Survey: Switzerland. *http://www.ilga.info/Information/*

Legal_survey/ilga_world_legal_survey% 20introduction.htm. Accessed June 21, 2006.
10. Harris SE. Military policies regarding homosexual behavior: An international survey. *Journal of Homosexuality.* 1991;21:70–71.
11. The World Sex Guide: Prostitution in Switzerland. Available at: *http://www. sexatlas.com/wsg/Switzerland.php*. Accessed June 24, 2006.

THAILAND

1. Legal Age of Consent. Available at: *http://www.ageofconsent.com/*. Accessed June 20, 2006.
2. Moreau R. Sex and death in Thailand. *Newsweek.* July 20, 1992:50–51.
3. Manderson L. Public sex performances in Patpong and explorations of the edges of imagination. *The Journal of Sex Research.* 1992;29:451–475.
4. Jackson P. Male Homosexuality in Thailand: An Interpretation of Contemporary Thai Sources. Elmhurst, NY: Global Academic Publishers;1989.
5. Pyne H. Reproductive experiences and needs of Thai women: Where has development taken us? In: Sen G, Snow RC, eds. *Power and Decision: The Social Control of Reproduction.* Boston, MA: Harvard University Press; 1994:19–41.
6. Godley J. Kinship networks and contraceptive choice in Nang Rong, Thailand. *International Family Planning Perspectives.* 2001;27:4–10.
7. Phoolcharoen W. HIV/AIDS prevention in Thailand: Success and challenges. *Science.* 1998;280:1873–1874.
8. UNAIDS/WHO Epidemiological Fact Sheets by Country. Available at: *http://www.who.int/*

hiv/pub/epidemiology/pubfacts/en/. Accessed June 22, 2006.
9. UNAIDS Fact Sheet: Asia. Available at: *http://www.unaids.org/en/Regions_Countries/ Regions/Asia.asp*. Accessed June 22, 2006.
10. Hanenberg R, Rojanapithayakorn W, Kunasol P, Sokal D. Impact of Thailand's HIV-control programme as indicated by the decline of sexually transmitted diseases. *Lancet.* 1994;344:243–245.
11. Sachs A. The last commodity: Child prostitution in the developing world. *World Watch.* 1994;7:24–30.
12. International Lesbian and Gay Association. World Legal Survey: Thailand *http://www.ilga.info/Information/ Legal_survey/ilga_world_legal_survey%20 introduction.htm*. Accessed June 21, 2006.
13. Seabrook J. Sex for sale, cheap thrills. *New Statesman & Society.* May 31, 1991:12–13.
14. Shetry A, Lee M, Vatiklotis M. Sex trade: For lust of money. *Far Eastern Economic Review.* December 14, 1995:22–23.
15. Hebert B. Kids for sale. *The New York Times.* January 22, 1996:A15.

TURKEY

1. Legal Age of Consent. Available at: *http://www.ageofconsent.com/*. Accessed June 20, 2006.
2. International update: Turkey to revise school virginity tests. *Contemporary Sexuality*. 1995;29:9.
3. Abboud M. Turkey: What price virginity? *Connexions*. 1993;38:12.
4. Senlet P, Cagatay L, Ergin J, Mathis J. Bridging the gap: Integrating family planning with abortion services in Turkey. *International Family Planning Perspectives*. 2001;27:90–96.
5. *Abortion laws in Europe*. National Abortion Campaign. London, England; 1995.
6. The Alan Guttmacher Institute. *Sharing Responsibility: Women, Society, and Abortion Worldwide*. New York: The Alan Guttmacher Institute; 1999.
7. News items: Sex education in Turkey. *Choices*. 1996;25:39.
8. International Planned Parenthood Federation. Country Profile: Turkey. Available at: *http://www.ippf.org*. Accessed June 28, 2006.
9. UNAIDS/WHO Epidemiological Fact Sheets by Country. Available at: *http://www.who.int/hiv/pub/epidemiology/pubfacts/en/*. Accessed June 22, 2006.
10. Aral SO, Fransen L. STD/HIV prevention in Turkey: Planning a sequence of interventions. *AIDS Education and Prevention*. 1995;7:544–553.
11. Turkey: Feminists, lesbians organize. *off our backs*. February 1996:7.
12. Dynes W, ed. *Encyclopedia of Homosexuality*. New York: Guilford; 1990:1329–1330.
13. Yuzgan A. Homosexuality and the police terror in Turkey. *Journal of Homosexuality*. 1993;24:159–169.
14. International Lesbian and Gay Association. World Legal Survey: Turkey. *http://www.ilga.info/Information/Legal_survey/ilga_world_legal_survey%20introduction.htm*. Accessed June 21, 2006.
15. Cowell A. 'Natasha Syndrome' brings on a fever in Turkey. *The New York Times*. April 17, 1993:28L.
16. Montefiore S. Call me madame. *The New Republic*. August 23, 1993:11.

UNITED KINGDOM

1. Legal Age of Consent. Available at: *http://www.ageofconsent.com/*. Accessed June 20, 2006.
2. The Alan Guttmacher Institute. *Sharing Responsibility: Women, Society, and Abortion Worldwide*. New York: The Alan Guttmacher Institute; 1999.
3. Media research Council. Sex at the Millennium. Available at: *http://www.mrc.ac.uk*. Accessed June 20, 2006.
4. OPCS, *Population Trends*. HMSO. 1993; 74.
5. Social Exclusion Unit. *Teenage Pregnancy*. London: The Stationary Office Bookshops; 1999.
6. Ingham R. Exploring interactional competence: Comparative data from the UK and The Netherlands on young people's sexual development. Paper presented at the International Academy of Sex Research;1998.
7. Wellings K. Field J, Johnson AM, Wadsworth J. *Sexual Behaviour in Britain*. London: Penguin; 1994.
8. Wellings K. Trends in contraceptive use since 1970. *British Journal of Family Planning* 1986;12:15–22.
9. Department of Health and Social Security. *Contraceptive Advice and Treatment of*

Young People Under 16. Health Circular HC 86; 1986.

10. Population Information Program. IUDs: An update. *Population Reports.* 1995;6:9.

11. Pappenheim K. Emergency contraception provision in the UK. *Planned Parenthood in Europe.* 1995;24:20–22.

12. UNICEF, *A League Table of Teenage Births in Rich Countries.* Florence, Italy: UNICEF Innocenti Centre; July 2002.

13. *Abortion laws in Europe.* National Abortion Campaign. London, England; 1995.

14. Berer M. Abortion in Europe from a woman's perspective. In IPPF Europe Region. *Progress Postponed: Abortion in Europe in the 1990s.* London: IPPF; 1993:31–46.

15. FDA approves RU 486. *Choices.* 2000;28:32.

16. Henshaw SK, Singh S, Haas T. Recent trends in abortion rates worldwide. *International Family Planning Perspectives.* 1999;25:44–48.

17. UNAIDS/WHO Epidemiological Fact Sheets by Country. Available at: *http://www.who.int/hiv/pub/epidemiology/pubfacts/en/.* Accessed June 22, 2008.

18. International Lesbian and Gay Association. World Legal Survey: United Kingdom. *http://www.ilga.info/Information/Legal_survey/ilga_world_legal_survey%20introduction.htm.* Accessed June 21, 2008.

19. Associated Press.*The Daily Press.* January 13, 2000:A8.

20. It's their business. *The Economist.* 2001;358:18.

21. Prostitution: Great Britain. Available at: *http://en.wikipedia.org/wiki/Prostitution.* Accessed June 28, 2008.

22. Holder A. Harsh red lights and boys in blue. *The Guardian.* May 12, 1992:36.

23. Easton S. *The Problem of Pornography.* London: Routledge; 1994:122–144.

24. Einsiedal E. The British, Canadian, and US pornography commissions and their use of social science research. *Journal of Communication.* 1988;38:108–111.

25. Petiti, J. *Rights of the Child: Child pornography on the Internet.* United Nations Economic and Social Council, December 24, 2004.

UNITED STATES

1. Legal Age of Consent. Available at: *http://www.ageofconsent.com/.* Accessed June 20, 2006.

2. The Alan Guttmacher Institute. *Sharing Responsibility: Women, Society, and Abortion Worldwide.* New York: The Alan Guttmacher Institute; 1999.

3. The Alan Guttmacher Institute. *Facts in Brief: Teen Sex and Pregnancy.* New York: The Alan Guttmacher Institute; 1996.

4. Singh S, Darroch J. Adolescent pregnancy and childrearing: Levels and trends in developed countries. *Family Planning Perspectives.* 2000;32:14–23.

5. Darroch J, Singh S, Frost J, Study Team. Differences in teenage pregnancy rates among five developed countries: The roles of sexual activity and contraceptive use. *Family Planning Perspectives.* 2001;33:244–250 & 281.

6. Henshaw SK. Unintended pregnancy in the United States. *Family Planning Perspectives.* 1998;30:24–29 & 46.

7. The Alan Guttmacher Institute. *Facts in Brief: Contraceptive Use.* New York: The Alan Guttmacher Institute; 1996.

8. Torres A, Forrest J. Family planning clinic services in the United States. *Family Planning Perspectives.* 1985;17:30.

9. NOT-2-LATE.com The Emergency Contraception Website. Available at: *http://ec.princeton.edu/.* Accessed June 22, 2008.

10. Petchesky RP. *Abortion and Women's Choice*. Boston: Northeastern University Press; 1985.

11. Althaus FA,. Henshaw SK. The effects of mandatory delay laws on abortion patients and providers. *Family Planning Perspectives*.1994;25:228–233.

12. Center for Reproductive Rights. *Abortion and the Law: Ten Years of Reform*. Available at: *http://www.crlp.org/wn_abortion.html*. Accessed June 22, 2008.

13. The Henry J. Kaiser Family Foundation. *Survey on Teens and Sex: What They Say Teens Today Need to Know, and Who They Listen To*. Menlo Park, CA: The Henry J. Kaiser Family Foundation; 1996.

14. The Alan Guttmacher Institute. *Facts in Brief: Induced Abortion*. New York: The Alan Guttmacher Institute; 2002.

15. FDA approves RU 486. *Choices*. 2000;28:32.

16. Sexuality Information and Education Council of the United States (SIECUS). Fact Sheet on Sexuality Education. Available at: *http://www.siecus.org/pubs/fact/fact0007.html*. Accessed June 20, 2008.

17. Office of the Surgeon General. The Surgeon General's Call to Action to Promote Sexual Health and Responsible Sexual Behavior 2001. Available at: *http://www.surgeongeneral. gov/library*. Accessed June 22, 2008.

18. UNAIDS Fact Sheet: North America, Western and Central Europe. Available at: *http://www.unaids.org/en/Regions_Countries /Regions/NthAmer_West_Cent_Europe.asp*. Accessed June 22, 2008.

19. UNAIDS/WHO Epidemiological Fact Sheets by Country. Available at: *http://www.who.int/ hiv/pub/epidemiology/pubfacts/en/*. Accessed June 22, 2008.

20. The Alan Guttmacher Institute. *Facts in Brief: Teenagers' Sexual and Reproductive Health*. Available at: *http://www.alanguttmacher.org/pubs/ fb_teens.html*. Accessed June 22, 2008.

21. Centers for Disease Control and Prevention. *Tracking the Hidden Epidemic: Trends in STDs in the United States, 2000*. Atlanta, GA: Centers for Disease Control and Prevention; 2000.

22. International Gay and Lesbian Human Rights campaign. Antidiscrimination Legislation. *http://www.iglhrc.org/site/iglhrc/ section.php?id = 1*. Accessed June 22, 2008.

23. National Gay and Lesbian Task Force. *http://www.ngltf.org*. Accessed June 22, 2008.

24. Shilts R. *Conduct unbecoming: Gays and lesbians in the U.S. military*. New York: St. Martin's Press; 1993.

25. U.S. Department of Defense. *Report on the military environment with respect to the homosexual conduct policy.* Office of the Inspector General; March 16, 2000.

26. Herrell R. The symbolic strategies of the Chicago's Gay and Lesbian Pride Day Parade. In Herdt G, ed. *Gay Culture in America*. Boston: Beacon Press; 1992.

27. Prostitutes' Education Network. Available at: *http://www.bayswan.org/penet.html*. Accessed June 24, 2008.

28. Kelly G. *Sexuality Today: A Human Perspective 8th edition*. New York: McGraw-Hill; 2006:464.

29. Feminists for free Expression. Feminism and Free Speech: Pornography. Available at: *http://www.ffeusa.org/html/statements/ statements_pornography.html*. Accessed June 22, 2008.

30. MiracleTS, Miracle AW, Baumeister RF. *Human Sexuality: Meeting Your Basic Needs*. Upper Saddle River, NJ: Prentice Hall; 2003:426.

31. MacKay J. Global sex: Sexuality and sexual practices around the world. *Sexual and Relationship Therapy*. 2001:16:71–82.

32. Strong B, DeVault C, Sayad BW., Yarber, W. *Human Sexuality, 5th edition*. New York: McGraw-Hill; 2006:660–661.

ZIMBABWE

1. Legal Age of Consent. Available at: *http://www.ageofconsent.com/*. Accessed June 20, 2006.
2. Kim YM. Promoting sexual responsibility among young people in Zimbabwe. International Family Planning Perspectives. 2001;27:11–18.
3. Carroll JL, Wolpe PR. *Sexuality and Gender in Society*. New York: Harper Collins Publishers; 1996:452,527,620–621.
4. Basset M. Zimbabwe: The social roots of AIDS. *UNESCO Courier*, June 1995.
5. Mensch B, Fisher A, Askew I, Ajayi A. Using situation analysis data to assess the functioning of family planning clinics in Nigeria, Tanzania, and Zimbabwe. *Studies in Family Planning*. 1994;25:18–32.
6. Piotrow PT, Kincaid DL, Hindin MJ, et al. Changing men's attitudes and behavior: The Zimbabwe male motivational study. *Studies in Family Planning*. 1992;23:365–375.
7. Henderson C. Condom vending machine joins fight against AIDS. *AIDS Weekly*. September 1992.
8. United Nations. *Abortion Policies: A Global Review*. New York: United Nations; 1992.189–191.
9. Center for Reproductive Laws and Policy. Reproductive Rights 2000: Moving Forward. Available at: *http://www.crlp.org*. Accessed October 29, 2002.
10. McCauley AP, Salter C. Growing numbers, diverse needs. *Population Reports*. 1995;23:3–11.
11. UNAIDS/WHO Epidemiological Fact Sheets by Country. Available at: *http://www.who.int/hiv/pub/epidemiology/pubfacts/en/*. Accessed June 22, 2006.
12. UNAIDS Fact Sheet: Sub-Saharan Africa. Available at: *http://www.unaids.org/en/Regions_Countries/Regions/SubSaharanAfrica.asp*. Accessed June 22, 2006.
13. International Lesbian and Gay Association. World Legal Survey: Zimbabwe. *http://www.ilga.info/Information/Legal_survey/ilga_world_legal_survey%20introduction.htm*. Accessed June 21, 2006.
14. The World Sex Guide. Prostitution in Zimbabwe. Available at: *http://www.sexatlas.com/wsg/Zimbabwe.php*. Accessed June 24, 2006.

INTERNATIONAL RESOURCES RELATED TO SEXUALITY

Alan Guttmacher Institute
Publishes *International Family Planning
Perspectives*
120 Wall Street, 21st floor
New York, NY 10005
USA
Tel: 212/248-1111
Website: *http://www.alanguttmacher.org*

**International Gay and Lesbian Human Rights
Commission**
80 Maiden Lane, Suite 1505
New York, NY 10038
USA
Tel: 212/268-8040
Website: *http://www.iglhrc.org*

**International Planned Parenthood Federation
(IPPF)**
4 Newhams Row
London SE1 3UZ
ENGLAND
Tel: 44-(0)20-7939-8200
Website: *http://www.ippf.org*

**United Nations Joint Programme on AIDS
(UNAIDS)**
20 Avenue Appia 1211
Geneva 27
SWITZERLAND
Tel: 41-22-791-3666
Website: *http://www.unaids.org*

United Nations Population Fund (UNFPA)
220 East 42nd Street
New York, NY 10017
USA
Tel: 212/297-5000
Website: *http://www.unfpa.org*

World Association of Sexual Health
Tezoquipa 26
Colonia La Joya
Delegacion Tlalapan
Mexico D.F. 14000
Mexico
Website: *http://www.worldsexology.org*

World Health Organization (WHO)
20 Avenue Appia 1211
Geneva 27
SWITZERLAND
Tel: 41-22-791-2111
Website: *http://www.who.int/en/*